DUNFERMLINE ABBEY FROM GLEN GARDENS : J CAMPBELL KERR

£2.70

The
Rowan Tree

ALONE in her place,
  She sways in the air,
Her blossoms like lace,
  Cream-tinted and rare,
The rain on her face,
  The breeze in her hair.

The cloud-shadows pace,
  Gigantic and free.
The wind-ripples trace
  A path on the sea,
And sunbeams embrace
  This magical tree.

In star-studded space
  Before life began,
Did God, in His grace,
  Far-sightedly plan
A tree robed in lace
  To captivate Man . . . ?
— *Brenda G. Macrow.*

People's Friend Annual

●

CONTENTS

BACK COVER The Old Brig o'Dee, Balmoral

Come Back My Love...

by GRACE MACAULAY

ZENA WEBSTER did not take defeat graciously.

"I come from a long line of fisher folk," she told Matthew Cameron grimly. "We don't believe in letting people get away with insults."

Matthew Cameron was having to hurry to keep up with her as she strode along the lane which led from the hotel to the village. He was getting more and more out of breath.

He would have liked to grab hold of her to slow her up — if not to stop her altogether. In fact, he would have liked nothing better than to hold her in his arms and kiss her. But Zena was the untouchable kind — as he had discovered time and again when he'd tried to get close to her during his holiday on the island.

Not that she was unfriendly, although he had wondered at times to what extent her friendliness was genuine, since it was part of her job as receptionist at her parents' hotel to be pleasant to the guests. Obliging, too, he thought ruefully, wishing he'd never told her that he'd like to go out in a boat on this, the last day of his holiday.

"There's one I've noticed and admired particularly," he had told Zena. "It's called the Stella Maris."

"No problem," Zena had assured him. "The Stella Maris belongs to my father's cousin — he often hires her out."

She had quoted the usual payment, which he had agreed was reasonable, but he had told her doubtfully, "I've never handled a boat that size."

"I have." Zena had given him one of her most brilliant smiles. "I'll take you out — we can go right round the island on a perfect day like today."

At once she had picked up the phone to call the owner.

"Hello, Gordon," she had said. "One of our guests would like to hire your boat for the day."

Then a frown had appeared on her face as she exclaimed, "But why not? I'll be taking him myself . . ."

Then she had spoken furiously to Matthew. "He hung up on me! Of all the nerve!"

She had dialled the number again, tapping her fingers impatiently, her temper rising as she received no reply.

"Right!" She had banged down the receiver. "We'll just go and see about this!"

And after a swift word of explanation to her mother she had stormed out of the hotel, Matthew following and attempting to convince her that a battle was not necessary.

"Surely the man is entitled to refuse to hire out his own boat?" Matthew tried to speak calmly and reasonably but the effect was rather spoilt by his puffing efforts to keep up with her fast pace.

"I disagree," she answered. "A boat for hire is a boat for hire."

Matthew took a glance at her grim face. Obviously he had no chance of influencing her. He capitulated abruptly.

"OK — but count me out," he said, and turned off the road to walk much more slowly towards the beach.

H E was glad to sit down on a large boulder a few yards away. He fought to get his breathing under control. Evidently he was not nearly as fit as he had hoped to be after recuperating for two weeks on the island.

The doctors had warned him that he must take things easy for a while after a bad bout of pneumonia. But somehow he suspected that it wasn't only the unaccustomed exercise which had affected him so much.

It was also the devastating effect of his attraction to Zena Webster.

As if to reinforce that knowledge, his heart began to turn somersaults as he heard her footsteps following him. She came to stand in front of him.

He looked up. She was standing with her hands on her hips watching him anxiously. Her face was bright pink and her eyes were an even brighter blue than usual.

He felt quite dazzled. And yet he was ashamed of his weakness. She thought nothing of rushing two miles or more to settle an argument. But he had hardly even covered a mile before he had given up. He was desperately afraid that he had gone down in her estimation.

He dreaded her scorn. She was so energetic, vital and brimful of laughter. He suddenly felt that he would die if she laughed at him.

But Zena wouldn't have embarrassed him for the world. With all her heart she was wishing that she could hold him in her arms and soothe away his distress. She had never been so close to tears in all her life.

In tones of deepest dejection she started to say, "My mother keeps telling me that I must learn to control my quick temper."

She paused uncertainly, realising that Matthew was looking past her with a curious expression on his face. She turned to follow the direction of his gaze. And there was the Stella Maris chugging by on the blue water!

The man at the wheel raised a hand in salute. Zena waved back automatically.

"So Gordon already had a hire," she said in vexed tones. "He might at least have said so."

Matthew almost reminded her that she had scarcely given the man a chance! But he wisely held his tongue and after a moment, Zena explained.

"They must have been in a hurry to catch the tide at the caves — that man, the passenger, is a geologist. He comes to the island every so often to study our caves."

She swung round to face Matthew.

"I'm so sorry," she said sombrely. "I wanted your last day to be special."

Alarmed to see tears glistening in her eyes, Matthew rose to his feet.

"It doesn't matter," he said, taking her in his arms at last. "I don't mind in the least."

And when she rested her head on his shoulder and made no move to get out of his embrace, he was encouraged to say, "As long as I'm with you, I'd be happy to spend the day right here."

She placed her hands against him and looked wistfully into his eyes.

"There are other boats for hire," she told him, "we could . . ."

But Matthew couldn't resist the lure of her lips. They were warm and sweet and responsive . . . yet it was a kiss which ended before it began.

"No —" She pulled away from him and went to sit on the large stone. She felt quite dizzy and her legs had turned to jelly.

"Why not, Zena?" Matthew sat down beside her and slid his arm across her shoulders. "You wanted me to kiss you, didn't you?"

"Maybe . . ." She hung her head, refusing to look at him and in a small forlorn voice she said, "You'll be leaving this island tomorrow."

"But I'll come back." He tried to draw her closer, talking persuasively. "My roots are here, you know that. I told you that day we went to see the house where my grandmother was born. I promised her that I'd find it and take some photographs. I tried to put my arm round you when we were looking at the house. I wanted to kiss you then . . ."

"I know." Zena sighed. And now she turned to gaze at him with infinite regret.

"It was an emotional moment, Matthew," she said. "You were thinking of a long-ago girl falling in love . . ."

"Yes, I was," he admitted, "but I was thinking about you, too. I believed that history was repeating itself, that I was falling in love with you."

SHE shook her head, not disbelievingly, but sadly. She was attracted to him, she could not deny it to her own heart. But she told him earnestly,

"This is a romantic island. People who come here from the mainland often get dreamy ideas." She gave a small eloquent shrug. "But we islanders are more the reserved sort."

"I've noticed," Matthew said heavily. Yet still he pleaded. "I won't go away and forget you. I will be back — and I'll write to you. Will you write back to me?"

"What would I write about?" Zena asked, her blue eyes wide with astonishment.

Matthew gazed at her helplessly. Anything, he wanted to plead, anything at all just so we keep a link between us. A cold sweat came out on his brow at the thought of leaving her — losing her. Then inspiration came.

"You could keep an eye open for any of my grandmother's relatives who might come back to the house," he suggested, adding, "that couple on the neighbouring croft were cagey, but they did tell us that the place still belongs to the Robertson family."

"Yes." Zena nodded, and then after a long silence, she said, "they would be your people, too — any relatives belonging to your grandmother."

Matthew watched her face, sensing some hidden meaning in her remark as he admitted, "That's true. But as I told you, I didn't even know of their existence until my grandmother talked my parents into sending me here to convalesce. And except for telling me the way to the house, she was extremely vague." He halted and gave a puzzled shrug.

"I wish I knew more," he finished regretfully.

"We guessed the rest between us, didn't we?" Zena sounded oddly subdued. "Your grandmother belonged to the island and your grandfather took her away."

Then abruptly, she demanded, "Do you think she has been longing always to come back? Did your grandfather forbid her to return?"

"No — my grandfather was no bully! She was always the bossy one of the two," Matthew answered swiftly, startled for the moment. Then he said reasonably, "She could have come back, she could have afforded a holiday. And even now there's nothing to prevent her, she is quite fit and healthy for her age."

Zena turned her gaze to the blue waters lapping at the shore.

"Some houses on this island have stood empty ever since I can remember."

She spoke in cool, remote tones, adding, "Mostly the old houses are left to fall into ruins."

And before he could comment, she went striding away back to the hotel.

▶ over

Next day Matthew went home feeling extremely despondent. His parents were concerned about his wan appearance. But they were slightly reassured when the doctor pronounced him fit to return to work.

"Perhaps you won't be so lackadaisical once your mind is occupied again," his mother remarked optimistically.

How could he tell his mother that his mind was totally preoccupied with a girl who seemed to care nothing for him?

He started to write to Zena. He had so much to say to her, his thoughts were for ever on the island with Zena . . . Then he would recall her question — *What would I write about?* And his spirits would sink and he would tear yet another page across and across.

ZENA searched eagerly through the mail every day. She didn't give up hope easily. But when two full weeks had gone by, an icy despair began to creep into her spirits.

She would find herself staring at Matthew Cameron's name and address in the hotel register and she would tell herself — all you have to do is pick up a pen and paper, a stamp doesn't cost much . . .

But what would she say to him?

I miss you. This island is a lonely place without you. I take the dogs out every day and I think about you all the time when I walk along the paths we walked together.

I stand every day at the jetty watching the boat bringing tourists to the island. I look for you among the passengers as they step ashore and in my heart I cry when I cannot see your face.

One day her mother said to her, "You look weary, Zena — why don't you take a rest this afternoon instead of tramping miles across the island?"

"I'd rather go out," Zena replied in a subdued voice and turned away from her mother's scrutiny.

Yesterday her father had remarked that she seldom lost her temper.

"You are not like yourself these days," he had said. "I hope you are not pining after that young jeweller who took such a fancy to you."

That afternoon, she deliberately avoided all the paths she had trodden with Matthew. No more pilgrimages, she told herself firmly. But on the way home she had to pass near the house where Matthew's grandmother was born.

She saw at once that the place looked different. Signs of occupancy included washing on the line — and Zena's heart began to pound as she saw an old woman sitting in the garden . . .

"I hope I'm not intruding." Zena felt incredibly timid as she approached.

"Not at all. I'm glad of someone to speak to." The woman smiled and invited Zena to sit down.

Out of politeness, Zena told the woman her name and where she lived.

"Yes, I could tell you were an islander," she said, smiling.

The woman seemed pleased and went on to tell Zena that her own name was Robertson and that her family had connections with the island going back generations.

"But we are the only ones who come home nowadays," she told the girl. "It is hard to break our link with the island. Sentiment draws us back every year to see the old place in spite of the high winds which are so bad for the rheumatics."

She paused, watching Zena enquiringly, sensing some tension in the atmosphere.

Zena's face was burning as she blurted out:

"I came here once to take photographs of your house . . . with one of our guests from the hotel. Matthew Cameron . . ." She halted and bit her lip nervously.

"Matthew Cameron? Did you say Matthew Cameron?" The old woman leaned forward, transfixing Zena with her eyes. "Do you mean Matthew Cameron the clockmaker?"

Zena shook her head. "No. He is a jeweller . . ."

But as she spoke, a shiver ran down her spine, for the old woman continued to stare at her.

Golden Showers

SHOWERS of golden roses,
  Tumble down a gable wall,
Dripping their tear-shaped petals
  On the blue hocks standing tall.
Drenching every leaf and stalk
  As they flutter on a tide,
To reach far into corners
  Where only shadows hide.
Forming pools of yellow brightness
  To light the dark beneath a tree,
Nature tries her very best to cheer,
  If we but use our eyes to see.

— *Katherine MacIntyre.*

MATTHEW set the elaborate alarm system before he locked up his father's shop. He was thinking of Zena. But tonight his thoughts were particularly poignant because he was carrying the photographs he'd taken of her in his pocket.

A phone call from his grandmother had reminded him.

"You were supposed to come and tell me all about your holiday on the island — did you find the house?"

"Yes, Grandma, I found it." His throat had constricted painfully as he told her. "I took some photographs. I'll get them developed and bring them round to show you."

So now as he drove towards her house he knew she would want to know about the girl who appeared in almost all the snapshots. He would be forced to admit that he'd fallen in love with Zena. His grandmother seldom asked questions but she had a way of getting information out of people, he knew.

So now as he drove towards her house he knew she would want to know about the girl who appeared in almost all the snapshots. He would be forced to admit that he'd fallen in love with Zena. His grandmother seldom asked questions but she had a way of getting information out of people, he knew.

But his grandmother didn't seem to notice Zena. It was the house which interested her. She studied one photograph for a long time through her magnifying glass.

"It looks so deserted," she murmured, then lifted another snap. "This girl . . . ?"

"She lives at the hotel." Matthew blushed awkwardly, and added, "There was nobody staying in the house."

"Nobody there at all?" Mrs Cameron's eyes brimmed suddenly as Matthew slowly shook his head. Then her voice quivered with emotion as she said, "I thought there would most surely be somebody left."

"Maybe they moved away," Matthew spoke sympathetically. "Families don't always stick to one house. You left — didn't you?"

And when he saw her turning to look up at the portrait of his grandfather, Matthew said, "I take it that my grandfather didn't belong to the island?"

And when she remained silent, he told her, "I did try to find out about the owners of the house. But the islanders have a way of avoiding direct questions. They are like you, Grandma. They close up like the proverbial clam if you try to ask the time of day!"

A fond smile curved the old woman's mouth.

"You sound just like your grandfather," she said softly and then her smile faded. "I suppose he had reason enough to be bitter about the island . . . At times I used to tease him and say — why not forgive them all? After all, you captured me in the end."

"Captured you?" Matthew echoed, round eyed with amazement.

"That was simply a figure of speech, Matthew," the old woman reproved him primly. But after a lengthy silence she began to speak in softly-reminiscent tones.

"I was seventeen the summer Matthew came to the island to repair the clock. My father didn't take an instant dislike to him. It was just that he'd expected an older man — the owner of the firm of clockmakers.

"But Matthew always believed my father disliked him. Personally I don't think my father would have had him put off the island if it hadn't been that we fell in love at first sight, Matthew and I . . . and my father would never have known that if my sister hadn't told him so."

This time she stayed silent so long that her grandson, on the edge of his chair, demanded.

"You say your father *put* him off the island . . . then how did he manage to capture you?"

"He saved his money until he could afford to pay a fisherman to row him back to the island." Mrs Cameron spoke as if in a dream.

14

"Did you know that he planned to do that?" Matthew asked insistently.

"I was hoping." His grandmother smiled. "My poor Matthew was seasick every inch of the way, it seemed a long journey to the mainland." She paused and then continued pensively.

"Maybe that was why he would never let me talk about our elopement. Men don't like to appear weak and helpless in front of their womenfolk."

"That is very true." Matthew gave her a broad grin and he came across to sit on the arm of her chair.

"Grandma," he went on, "will you look at the photographs again? Take a good look at the girl, please."

He waited impatiently while she obeyed him.

"Do you see the way she is looking at the camera?" he asked urgently then hesitated for a moment.

"Would you say she is looking towards the photographer as if . . . as if she cared?"

"I would say so," Mrs Cameron spoke cautiously, and then glancing up at her grandson, she gave a positive opinion. "I would say so quite definitely, Matthew."

"So would I, Grandma." He spoke on notes of sheer joy and bent to kiss her cheek, promising softly, "I'll bring her to meet you very soon."

But now his grandmother gripped his hand with a fiercely unexpected strength.

"My heart was torn in two." Her voice was low and vibrant. "I loved your grandfather deeply, I adored the ground beneath his feet — but I loved my own people, too. I loved the island where I was born . . ."

ZENA WEBSTER stood on the jetty watching the boat coming in. When it left again her letter would be on its way to Matthew . . .

She had ended the letter with the words — *I do hope that your grandmother will want to be reunited with her sister and brother. I can't tell you how pleased they were to have news of their sister.*

Writing the letter had taken Zena hours last night. She still wondered if she ought to have copied it out again or perhaps she could have added something like — *I hope to hear from you soon.*

She was watching the post office. She did not see Matthew disembarking.

Suddenly, as if my magic, he was standing in front of her, speaking her name, making it sound like the sweetest word on earth.

"You came back!" she breathed.

She went into his arms and they held each other close.

"I couldn't stay away." Matthew put his lips on hers.

But after a second, he looked solemnly into her eyes.

"I want to take you away," he said, "but I shall always bring you back to this island."

Zena clung to him rapturously. She would never let him go. □

AGE DOESN'T

W HILE the car was stopped at the traffic lights, Maria glanced idly into the window of a china shop, and a fleeting, elusive memory made her say:

"I had the strangest dream last night."

She spoke the words slowly because she couldn't precisely recall the dream, although the mood of it was in her head and she sensed that there could be some significant portent — if only she could catch at it.

Then the lights changed and the car shot forward. She turned her head — in time to observe an expression of long-suffering boredom on Donald Rankine's face.

Then it was gone and he was giving her a sidelong, apologetic grin and telling her in the same instant:

"The car is due to go in for a service — the clutch is slipping. Just as well we had our seat-belts on."

Maria said nothing. Is it possible, she wondered, to feel frozen and shattered at the same time?

It didn't occur to her to feel insulted. She was far too disappointed in herself. She had let herself down. She had allowed Donald Rankine to discover that she was a dull, boring person.

She didn't know what had made her come out with that utterly stupid comment about a dream. She had been thinking of mentioning that highbrow book she had taken out of the library last night. The title escaped her now. But what did it matter?

That look on Donald Rankine's face had robbed her of any desire to impress him. It was as if all hope had been torn from her heart.

"Here you are then, safe and sound." Donald's voice broke into her thoughts as he stopped the car outside the shop where she worked.

"Yes, right. Thank you," Maria said, and was sure that

COUNT !

by
ELIZA
YEAMAN

her face must be crimson as she fumbled with the seat-belt and then got clumsily out of the car.

She had never imagined that she'd say to herself, as she did in the shop doorway, thank goodness tomorrow is my last day.

Yet it was not true . . . she had been lucky to be sent to the dress shop for three months' work experience.

She liked the job and got along well with the other assistants. And until today, there had been the additional thrill of her lift every morning with Donald Rankine, who lived next door to her in the village.

She hung up her coat and looked in the mirror to smooth her hair, recalling that moment of incredulous excitement when her father had come in from the garden and told her:

"Donald says he will take you to work in the mornings."

And Maria's mother had said warmly, "That's very good of him."

"He doesn't start work until nine-thirty and he goes along the High Street anyhow." Her father had turned then from drying his hands and there had been a twinkle in his eye. "Donald could hardly believe that you're old enough to start work."

Then her parents had both gazed at her fondly. She could sense they were remembering how she used to hero worship Donald Rankine, how at six years old she had wept and wept when he went away to university.

By the time he came home at the end of his first term, Maria had entered a phase of extreme shyness which virtually put an end to their friendship. But in the years which followed, she had heard either from his parents or her own about his career in electronics that had taken him all over the world. Then last year he had come home because of his father's failing health to take his place in the family electrical firm.

I N the narrow locker-room now, Maria pressed both hands against her heart as she tried to recall that moment last winter when she had caught sight of him in the snow-filled garden.

She closed her eyes tightly, forcing herself to recapture the vision. He was tall and bronzed from the tropical sun, smiling at her from blue eyes . . . the man of my dreams. The knowledge had been breathtaking . . .

The cloakroom door flew open suddenly and with a humorous lilt to her voice, the shop manageress, Mrs Stanley, was saying:

"So here you are, Maria! You can stop praying now and come into my office — I have some good news for you."

Praying, Maria thought as she followed the older woman. How could she have imagined that I was praying?

"There was a call from head office about you," Mrs Stanley told her. "I was told to inform you that on my recommendation, you are to be offered a contract of employment."

Maria's eyes opened wide. She tried to think of something to say.

My Lovely Granddaughter

THE housework is done and everything shining,
I think I'll have a half-hour's reclining.
But there's a knock on the door and somebody small
Is waiting to tumble into the hall.

Two laughing eyes, an infectious grin,
"Come on, Grandma, let me in."
"You can't come in, because I'm out."
"Don't be silly, Grandma!" is the shout.

So you open the door and over the step
Comes one small bundle brimming with pep.
"Have you got any biscuits for me today?"
"None at all, darling," I hasten to say.

So off she goes to the biscuit tin,
Lifts off the lid and peeps within.
"Grandma, you have! Can I have two?"
"Of course, my petal, there's plenty for you."

There's crumbs on the floor and beakers of pop,
Excuse me a moment while I get the mop,
There's a mess on the table, hand-marks on the door,
Just look around, I am tidy no more.

Then she gives me a kiss and hugs me so tight,
And waves and waves till she's out of sight.
So I clean up the house, I'm tidy once more
But, please, God, keep her knocking at my front door.

— *Betty Clifton.*

Age Doesn't Count!

Then she felt her eyes filling up with tears and the older woman said reprovingly:

"What an emotional girl you are, first praying, now crying! Still, I suppose it's not every day a girl gets a permanent job."

"Thank you, Mrs Stanley." Maria gulped back the dryness in her throat and in a panic in case the older woman might change her mind, she assured her unsteadily.

"I promise you I'll always do my best to be worthy . . ." Then she halted, unable to think of suitable words.

"I have confidence in you." Mrs Stanley smiled and nodded to show that she quite understood. "Of course, you realise that you'll be expected to start work at nine o'clock from now on."

Maria listened in a daze to all the details of her new status in the shop. Then later, the other girls clustered round to offer their congratulations and Maria completely forgot about Donald Rankine and that unguarded look which had put a full stop to all her efforts to impress him.

At teatime when she gave her parents the good news about her job, they were as pleased and proud as she had known they would be.

"Now you'll be able to go into town in the mornings with me," her father said, and as he gave a satisfied nod, his wife seemed to echo his thoughts.

"Yes," she said, "that will be much better." Then she stopped and bit her lower lip, giving Maria an apologetic glance.

Maria gazed from one to the other of them and demanded to know.

"What's going on? What have you against me going with Donald all of a sudden?"

She intercepted a look between her parents, like some sort of warning signal. Then they spoke simultaneously.

"We can't help noticing that you're developing a crush on him." Her mother spoke anxiously.

"He is too old for you, Maria." Her father seemed equally anxious.

Maria knew that her face must be scarlet but somehow she kept her voice steady while she answered.

"What you mean is — I'm too young for him, and not nearly clever enough!"

S HE pushed back her chair and hurried away to the privacy of her bedroom. A forlorn sensation of loneliness swept over her.

Nobody understands, she thought sadly as she changed into casual clothes and brushed her hair.

Not long ago she could have confided all her confused thoughts in her friend, Julie — but since Maria had started work and Julie remained at school, the two best friends had lost some of the affinity which had previously existed between them.

Now Maria's mother came into the room after a tap on the door.

"Julie is here to go with you to the youth club. She is talking to your father in the garden."

Giving her daughter a troubled look, she added:

"You are better to go around with friends your own age."

Maria knew that her mother needn't have come all the way upstairs just to tell her that. It was an attempt to make peace and Maria made the effort to smile.

"Thanks, Mum," she said. "I'm all ready."

The youth club was no different, Maria told herself, and I haven't really changed. Most of the crowd were still at school but quite a few were now working or at training colleges. There was no reason for her to feel such a sense of isolation and dissatisfaction, she thought later as she lay awake studying the events of the day.

Next morning she was up early. You're very lucky, she told herself firmly, you might have been feeling sad and miserable because this was the last day at the shop. But in the mirror she could clearly see the sadness in her own face. It was as if her heart utterly refused to be happy.

She dressed with care and tried not to imagine the admiring look she would receive from Donald Rankine. She didn't mind the fact that he never paid her any compliments, never said very much at all to her. It was just enough to be near him for the precious half-hour every morning . . .

She got into the car beside him today. Her voice sounded curiously remote as she greeted him and her smile felt more like a spasm of pain. Then while she was reaching round for the seatbelt, Donald said:

"You look lovely this morning, Maria." She turned, and their eyes met. He said, "Your father told me last night about your new job. Congratulations."

Maria had to look down to click the seatbelt into place. She murmured her thanks. She was blushing. And her heart seemed to be filled with butterflies.

"The car is behaving better today, you'll notice," Donald said as they drove out of the village. "Have you recovered from that scare I gave you at the traffic lights yesterday?"

"Scare . . . ?" Maria glanced at him in confusion.

"Don't you remember?" He turned towards her briefly. "You were telling me about your strange dream when I almost jolted you out of your seat. You didn't utter another word until you were safely at the shop."

▶ *over*

PARTNERQUOTES

GARBO

1928: *"I suppose you have heard about me and a certain actor (Gilbert) . . . I am not going to be married . . ."*
1950s: *"I am for ever running away from something or somebody. Subconciously, I have always known that I was not destined for real and lasting happiness."*
Did you know that Garbo actually said: *"I want to be LET alone?"*

GILBERT

1928: *"She says she'll marry if I let her retire from the screen. She hates acting. She hates Hollywood and everything in it. She wants to buy half of Montana and turn it into a wheat farm. She keeps saying 'You're in love with Garbo the actress' and I say 'You're damn right!' "*
1929: John Gilbert married Ina Claire.

GRETA GARBO & JOHN GILBERT — ROMANCE THAT NEVER WAS

"Yes, I remember," Maria replied slowly, her thoughts in a ferment. "But I wasn't frightened. I — I thought you seemed bored at the idea of hearing about a silly dream."

"What made you think that?" He looked and sounded alarmed.

"I don't know now," Maria spoke uncertainly. "Maybe I misread the expression on your face. Or maybe I just realised that other people's dreams are not very interesting. And in any case, I couldn't recall any of the details of my dream."

"But you're not other people," Donald assured her swiftly. "I'm always interested in everything about you."

"I didn't know that." Maria's voice was low and wondering. She stared at his profile — why was he looking so stern? And puzzled, she saw that his hands were clenched white around the steering wheel.

SHE moved her head to gaze at the road beyond and tried to think of something to say. She wished that he would speak. Surely there must be some way to break this silence between them?

All too soon they were approaching her destination. He was stopping the car. They faced each other very solemnly for a long tense moment. Then Donald said, as if it was not at all what he wanted to say:

"Don't work too hard in your new job, now."

That brought a smile to Maria's lips and a sparkle to her eyes.

"Don't worry, I won't," she answered, and as he responded to her smile her heart seemed to be caught in a beam of light.

"I shall miss talking to you in the mornings," she told him with a rush of confidence. Then as if the question opened up a million possibilities, she asked him, "Will you miss hearing all my chatter?"

He nodded and Maria had an intuitive sense that he hadn't intended to tell her.

"I told your father that I would be quite happy to go into my office earlier, but he prefers to drive you himself from now on. I couldn't very well argue . . ."

"No!" Maria was subdued for a moment. Then an irrepressible smile tugged at the corners of her mouth.

"If it's a good day tomorrow I expect you will be out doing some gardening!" she said.

She got out of the car quickly and they exchanged a wave and a smile before he drove away.

We have two great advantages, she thought, we live next door to each other — and I shall definitely, positively, get older!

She counted out seventeen paces on her way into the shop. Age doesn't count when you love somebody, she told herself confidently.

And in the locker-room, as she took off her coat, she decided, I shall be sensible and mature at all times.

But she had no way of controlling the singing in her pulses and her heart dancing to the rhythm of her thoughts. He loves me and I love him! □

by CHRISTINE
NICOLSON

A
Family Affair

THERE wasn't much that went on at home that escaped Lynn
MacNab's notice. So when her mother started slamming doors,
her father retreated behind his paper for hours at a time and
conversation was reduced to "Pass the salt" and "Turn that television

down!" — well, she had the distinct impression there was something
wrong!

"It isn't as if they don't usually argue," she confided in her
grandmother, when she called in on her way home from school one
afternoon. "They do — quite a lot."

"So what's the problem?" Meg Riley prompted.

"Well, this time it's different," Lynn explained. "Normally when
they have an argument the whole street knows about it! But it never
lasts long. It's usually something trivial, too, and they have a good
laugh about it afterwards."

"But it's not like that this time?" Meg queried.

"No, it's not." Lynn sighed. "This awful silence has gone on since
Monday, and I've had enough!"

After Lynn had set out for home, forgetting the usual cheery wave
that her gran always loved to see, Meg gave the matter some
thought.

That sulky kind of behaviour just wasn't like her daughter — Joan
had never been one to prolong a quarrel. Nor had Martin, come to
that. Still, it would probably blow over — and it was none of her
business anyway.

But when Lynn called the following week, it seemed that things
were just the same.

"I don't know what to do, Gran," she wailed. "I tried talking to
them both but got nowhere. I asked Dad what was wrong. 'Ask your
mother,' he said. So I did. 'Nothing to do with me,' she said. 'Ask
your father'."

Meg almost smiled at the sixteen-year-old's take off of her parents,
but realised this wasn't a time for humour.

"Honestly, it's awful." Lynn looked at her grandmother. "I don't
suppose you could do something?" she said hopefully. "They'd listen
to you. Tell them to stop being so stupid."

Meg looked thoughtful. It had always been her policy not to
interfere. She knew from experience how much trouble a well-
meaning mother-in-law could cause. Her own had given rise to more
problems between herself and Davie than they'd ever created by
themselves.

"Oh, I don't think . . ." she began, then stopped when she saw the
hurt in her granddaughter's eyes. "OK, I'll see what I can do."

IT wasn't easy for Meg to find an opportunity to talk to her
daughter alone. Joan's full-time job was demanding and she had
little free time. But finally the chance arose the following
Sunday, just before dinner.

Martin was on the golf course, a favourite haunt these days, and
Lynn was out in the back garden.

"Joan . . ." Meg began tentatively. "There's nothing wrong, is
there?"

"Wrong, Mum?" Joan's voice was immediately tense. "Why should there be anything wrong?"

"Well, Lynn said . . ."

"Oh, Lynn gets all sorts of daft ideas."

"She's really worried, you know," Meg said softly. And when Joan turned to face her, there were tears in her eyes.

"Oh, Mum!" she cried. "It's awful. I don't know what to do!"

"Take a seat and tell me all about it," Meg advised, pouring out tea for them both. "It can't be that bad!"

"You don't know the half of it!" Joan wiped her eyes and joined her mother at the kitchen table. "The fact is . . . Martin's job's on the line. His firm is pulling out of Britain."

"Oh, dear, I *am* sorry." Meg sympathised. "But he'll easily get another job. He's still young, and he's well qualified — "

"But there's more to it than that, Mum," Joan interrupted. "They've offered him another job — in Toronto!"

"In Toronto! Oh, Joan . . . !"

"And he says he's taking it! He didn't even consult me — he just said we should go. He thinks it's a marvellous opportunity!"

"And you don't?" Meg looked at her daughter.

"No, I don't!" Joan insisted. "I'm perfectly happy here. I love my job, my home and my friends. I don't want to leave Scotland. A couple of weeks' holiday abroad is quite enough for me.

"And what about Lynn? She'll be sitting her exams soon. This couldn't come at a worse time for her. And anyway, Mum, I couldn't leave you."

"That's not the point, Joan. I'm the least of your considerations. Have you told Lynn yet?"

"No, we haven't."

"You should."

"Yes, I know."

Just then Lynn popped her head round the back door.

"Dinner ready yet?"

"In about half an hour."

"You two been talking?" she demanded, coming right into the kitchen and taking a biscuit from the

Winter Beauty

SWIFTLY, silently, falling snow
　　Lays a white cover over all,
　　Outlining stark hedges, high and
low;
Flake upon flake, the land's disguised
　　As the deep, blue-shadowed drifts
grow.

Hexagonal flakes, drifting down
Hide winter's gaunt, brown, bareness,
　　Robe each tree in a white, lace
gown
And top the verdant, swaying firs
　　With a delicate, filigree crown.

　　Born in a snowy, northern spa,
Each tiny flake itself a gem
　　Of perfect shape, an ice-bound star;
Each individual pattern blessed
　　With crystal beauty, from afar.
　　　　　　　　— *Gillian Riddle.*

tin. "I hope so. It's about time somebody did in this house!" Meg drew out another chair from the table.

"Go on," she encouraged. "Sit down, Lynn. Now tell the lass, Joan."

As Joan quickly outlined the situation, Lynn's expression changed from astonishment, to disbelief — to dismay.

"Oh, help," she muttered. "Oh, boy! No wonder this hasn't blown over!"

"Your father has to give them his final decision tomorrow," Joan finished. "And according to him, it's Toronto, and that's that!"

L YNN couldn't sleep that night. She'd gone up to bed early, but the sound of her parents' raised voices kept her awake. The arguing had gone on for ages, but finally she'd heard footsteps on the stairs. They'd paused momentarily outside her bedroom door, then moved on, and at last an uneasy silence had fallen on the house.

Sometime after midnight, Lynn dropped off into a disturbed sleep, only to waken with a start a few hours later. For an instant her mind was blissfully clear of worry, but then the day's events came crashing in on her, and she tossed and turned and sleep just wouldn't come.

Eventually, when half her bedclothes lay in a heap on the floor and a chill had set in, making her shiver, she decided to get up.

She threw her dressing-gown round her shoulders, then switched on her electric blanket before heading downstairs. A hot drink would help.

A light shone out from under the kitchen door. Obviously someone was still up . . .

When Lynn saw her father slumped wearily over the kitchen table, his head buried in his hands, she felt tears sting her eyes. It was hard to equate this dejected, tired man with the active, cheerful father she'd idolised all her life.

At once her heart went out to him.

"Oh, Dad!" She went over and put her arms round him. "Why on earth didn't you tell me?" I'm old enough now to know what's going on. It might have helped you and Mum to talk things over with me."

Martin took his daughter's hand.

"There's nothing you can do, Lynn," he said simply. "You can't keep my job open for me here — and you can't change my mind about going to Canada either," he added quickly, as she opened her mouth to interrupt.

"I know your mother thinks we shouldn't go," he went on. "She's made that very plain. But what do you think, Lynn? Don't you like the idea of a new life abroad? You'd have a tremendous future. And they tell me Toronto's a lovely city.

"We'll have a great life there — this new job is a step up, and much better paid. We'll have all the things we've ever wanted."

"To be honest, Dad," Lynn said slowly, "I'm very happy here. I don't really want to go anywhere else. I guess I'm just a homebird like Mum."

"Oh, you just don't understand, Lynn!" Martin shook his head. "You don't seem to realise what it'll be like if we stay here and I'm out of work."

He looked round the large kitchen, with all the mod cons anyone could wish for.

"For a start, the house would have to go," he said flatly. "We couldn't afford it. And there'd be no more new clothes or fancy holidays — "

"That doesn't matter, Dad," Lynn broke in. "And anyway, Mum works. She's got a good job." ▶ *over*

★ PARTNERQUOTES ★

1942: Their first meeting on the set of "Woman Of The Year." *"You're rather short, aren't you?" said she.*
"Don't worry, Honey," said he. "I'll cut you down to my size."

TRACY

1946: *"There is conceit in all of us, I suppose, and I found that it was very pleasant to be applauded."*
50s: When asked by Laurence Olivier about his habit of using little make-up, if he ever felt naked. *"Only when I have to say a lousy line."*
60s: Referring to the film star era that had come from the 30s. *"When I go, a whole epoch will have ended."*
Timeless: *"Of all talents, acting is the least. Life's what's important: birth and love and pain and then death. Acting's just waiting for a custard pie. That's all . . ."*

HEPBURN

50s: *"To most men I'm a nuisance, because I'm so busy I get to be a pest. But Spencer is so masculine that once in a while he rather smashed me down, and there's something nice about me when I'm smashed down."*
1967: Shortly after his death, on hearing she had won an Oscar for "Guess Who's Coming To Dinner" — **their last film together.**
"Did Mr Tracy win it, too?"
"No," was the reply.
"Well, that's OK," she said. "I'm sure mine is for the two of us."
1982: *"I do have one skirt. I wear it at funerals . . ."*
1983: *"The only reason I wore pants was that I couldn't keep my stockings up. The garters and all that stuff kept slipping."*
Timeless: *"Spence? I'll miss him every day as long as I live."*

SPENCER TRACY & KATHARINE HEPBURN — A LOVE THAT LASTED

"But it's not enough, Lynn! I don't want to take a step backwards now. I've worked too hard to let it all slip away!"

"But, Dad, we're *happy* here!"

"Maybe just now — but if things change you won't be so happy. I'm just being practical, Lynn. I know what I'm doing, and I've made up my mind.

"We're going to Canada and that's all there is to it. The quality of our life is what's important — and I don't want that to change."

Lynn looked at her father and shook her head. He was obviously in no mood to listen. If her mother hadn't managed to change his mind in the past few weeks, nothing *she* could say would make any difference.

She made them both a hot drink, then headed for the door.

"I'm going up now, Dad." She blew him a kiss. "Try to get some sleep. You look worn out."

THE following morning was the kind of Monday best forgotten. The entire family slept in, the milkman was late, and it was teeming down with rain.

Martin, always the first to leave the house, was already ten minutes behind schedule when he rushed out to the car, only to discover that it wouldn't start. Not mechanically minded, he was at a complete and utter loss.

Ten minutes later, the battery completely dead, he resigned himself to failure — just as his wife and daughter left the house.

"I'll have to get the bus," he muttered. "I'll come with you."

Joan and Lynn exchanged glances. It was practically the first thing he'd said to them all morning.

Five silent minutes took them to Lynn's school. She gave them both a quick hug before hurrying in through the gates. At once she was swallowed up by a gang of chattering schoolgirls, eager to catch up on the weekend's news.

"She's popular, our Lynn." Joan gave Martin a searching look. "Seems a pity she'll have to leave all her friends."

"Excuse me! Hello!"

A voice from behind made them look round. A young woman was hurrying towards them.

"You're Lynn MacNab's parents, aren't you? I'm Mrs Drew, her form teacher — we met at the school fête. I won't keep you a minute . . . I just wondered if you were going to make it to the parents and teachers meeting tonight. Lynn didn't seem too sure if you'd be able to come . . ."

Martin glanced at Joan, feeling uncomfortable. He vaguely remembered Lynn mentioning something about this a few weeks ago.

"Oh, yes . . ." He cleared his throat. "I'm sure we'll manage."

"Oh, good." Mrs Drew smiled. "It's to discuss next year's course, and it's rather important that Lynn makes the right decisions.

"To be perfectly honest, I think she could turn her hand to anything. She's a very clever girl, you know." She glanced at her watch. "Sorry to keep you. See you tonight then."

"We'd better not miss that bus." Joan turned to Martin, annoyed at herself for forgetting the meeting. "We're late enough as it is."

A long queue was waiting when they reached the bus stop.

"At least we haven't missed it," Joan said, greeting several of the commuters who turned to say hello.

"Do you know all these people?" Martin asked, surprised.

"Oh, yes," Joan said airily. "Some of them are quite old friends."

Martin looked at his watch impatiently. It was so cold just standing about waiting. He stamped his feet and tried to keep warm.

He honestly couldn't remember the last time he'd used public transport. He'd had the luxury of the car for so long. Another good reason for accepting the job in Canada — if he didn't, the car would have to go.

Mind you, he'd be the only one to miss it. Lynn always walked to school, and Joan caught the bus to her work in the High Street.

The bus came at last and they found seats on the busy lower deck. At the next stop a woman got on and sat in front of Joan. She turned to her immediately.

"Have a good weekend, Joan?"

Joan forced a smile. "Oh, yes, lovely, thanks. Just the usual."

"Can you meet me for lunch later? I've loads to tell you!"

"Sorry, Barbara." Joan shook her head. "I've got a working lunch today with an important client. It'll make a big difference to the firm if we get the contract."

But will I be here to see it, she thought angrily.

"Have you applied for that promotion yet?"

Joan nodded. "Yes, I should know next week."

"Great. I'm sure you'll get it, after all you've done for them."

"Thanks, I hope so. Anyway, how about lunch tomorrow?"

Barbara grinned. "Fine. Usual time? Usual place?"

Joan nodded. "Yes, that's perfect."

"Right, I'm away." Barbara jumped up. "See you tomorrow!"

She bounded off and Martin leaned over.

"Who was that?"

"Barbara Gordon. Just a friend I've got to know — we've been travelling together for five years."

"I've never met her."

"No, well, we generally meet at lunchtimes, and on the bus, of course. I've told you about her before. You just never listen!"

"And what about this business lunch? And the promotion you're after? You've never mentioned it to me!"

"Well, I've had other things on my mind lately!"

"OK, well, tell me now."

"Oh, it's nothing much. I've been handling quite a few of the big accounts lately, and doing rather well. The promotion was meant to be a surprise — if I got it. But then, you seem to have other plans for my future."

Martin said nothing.

"Look, here's my stop now," Joan said, rising. She looked at her husband steadily. "Think about things, Martin. *Please.*"

MARTIN watched her as she made her way down the passage, pausing briefly to exchange a few words with an elderly lady.

Then, joining the waiting group at the door, she burst out laughing at something somebody said.

All at once Martin felt incredibly lonely. Joan seemed to know so many people he'd never even seen before! Mind you, Joan never had any trouble making friends . . .

That was where they differed. Martin's friends were the people he'd grown up with, gone to school with, worked beside — never anyone he met by chance. He wasn't particularly outgoing — he'd never felt the need. And anyway, Joan had always been his best friend.

Martin got off at the bus stop and walked the last few hundred yards to his office block. It was different not coming to work by car. A lot of things were different today . . .

He had to admit he'd had his eyes opened this morning. There was Lynn, his precious daughter, about to make one of the most important decisions of her young life, and he hadn't even cared enough to remember.

And Joan, who he thought he knew better than anyone — she had a responsible, satisfying career, and he'd scarcely been aware of it! He'd never thought she had much of a life outside the home — he thought her job was just something she did to fill in the empty hours.

How wrong could he be . . . ? And all those friends. No wonder his wife and daughter didn't want their lives to change!

Suddenly, something he'd said to Lynn in the middle of the night came rushing back to him. *The quality of our life is what's important.*

But what exactly does that mean, he thought, as he stepped into the lift and pressed the button for the sixth floor. Quality surely means family and friends, being content with what you've got. Quality is caring enough to take others' feelings into consideration, he thought grimly. And I've not been doing that.

Clearly now, he could see that all the arguments he'd used for going to Canada had been selfish. He couldn't face the loss of status that would come with the loss of his job. That was the real reason for wanting to go. The drop in prestige . . . the loss of his house, all the material things he'd worked for . . .

It hadn't hit him till now that Joan and Lynn would be losing so much more if they went, than he would if they stayed!

So what if he had to start from scratch? Surely he'd find something he could do? Work for himself, perhaps. He had the skills. And if Joan got this promotion she was after, perhaps they could afford to stay where they were. And if not . . .

Well, the house was far too big for them anyway. And if they had to sell the car? Well, Joan seemed to manage all right travelling by bus!

It wasn't going to be easy turning down this Canadian job. There was something deep down inside him which longed to respond to the challenge. But maybe there was an even tougher challenge to be faced at home . . .

Martin took a deep breath and knocked on the manager's office door.

Joan and Lynn were sitting at the kitchen table when Martin arrived home. Neither made a move to greet him when he came in, and he could see that Joan had been crying.

"I leave in a month's time," he said bluntly.

Joan gasped and shot him a look of utter despair.

"The redundancy money is all agreed. It should be a big help. Oh, and I called in at the job centre on the way home. I had an idea I wanted to discuss with them, and they were very encouraging."

Joan jumped up from the table and ran to her husband's waiting arms.

"Oh, thank goodness, Martin!" she almost cried with relief.

"Does this mean we're not going, Dad?" Lynn asked, her eyes shining.

Martin nodded. "We're staying right here," he said softly. "I just couldn't do it. Not now that my wife will soon be running that agency with one hand tied behind her back!"

He hugged Joan close for a moment, then released her.

"Right, let's get some tea on the go. We've got a date tonight, remember? You're not the only one going places, Joan."

He winked at Lynn. "Our daughter's got a great future ahead of her!" □

When The Wallflowers Bloom

WALLFLOWERS glowing
In the spring sunshine,
Fresh and fragrant
From an April shower,
Each petal diamonded
With a sparkling raindrop,
Oh, how we love you,
Each velvety flower!

Orange, white and yellow,
Rose-pink, and crimson,
And bronze — perhaps loveliest
Wallflowers of all!
Massed close together
In a wide border,
Backed by a venerable
Old stone wall.

Gillyflowers, they called you
In days long forgotten,
But gillyflowers, or wallflowers,
Each well-beloved name,
Evokes such a memory
Of softness and sweetness,
Without you, springtime
Would never be the same!
— Kathleen O'Farrell.

31

Melanie's Magic Wish

SIX-YEAR-OLD Melanie held her breath as the man turned his head sharply to stare at the clump of bushes behind which she was hiding.

She wasn't doing any harm — not even trespassing really — because though the bush was in the cottage garden, she wasn't. But she knew that grown-ups didn't like being watched.

It wasn't fair, she grumbled silently, as the man picked up a stone and held it over the hole.

There was a loud plop and the man looked up, a huge smile on his face, before hurrying away round the corner of the cottage. Melanie waited, thinking deeply.

A large hole? The plop? Melanie looked at the short row of stone cottages, with their tiny windows, and steps that went down to the doors instead of up as they did in any self-respecting house, and she remembered her mother telling her that the cottages were very old.

Could that hole be a well?

Melanie had seen a well once. They'd gone on a coach to a village where most of the houses were like these cottages. They'd had

by Phyllis Demaine

33

tea, she remembered, scones with cream and jam — oh, yummy! And there'd been a well in the garden where the tea tables were. There'd been a notice beside the well, and everyone had thrown money in and made wishes.

You could see the coins on the concrete bottom. There were lots of silver coins, but Mummy had only let her throw in a penny, and Daddy had said that as she hadn't anything big to wish for a penny would be enough. And he and Mummy had smiled, and held hands, and . . .

Melanie didn't realise she'd left her hiding place until the man spoke.

"It's a well," he said, and Melanie thought he sounded excited. Too excited to notice that she was inside the garden.

"I know,". she said cautiously.

"I just moved those great slabs of stone and there it was," he went on, almost as if he didn't realise Melanie was only a little girl. "Must have been here for ages! I think I'll build a little wall round it. Make a feature of it."

Melanie forgot where she was.

"What's a feature?" she asked. "I thought that meant your eyes or your nose."

Toby Stanton chuckled.

"It's the same sort of thing, in a way," he explained. "It means something of interest, something people want to see."

"Lots of people wanted to see the wishing well, all the coaches were full. Is yours a wishing well?"

"I don't know. I haven't tried wishing. But I don't think I want coachloads of people coming here. Perhaps I won't advertise. I'll just build a wall, like I said."

"Can I watch?"

TOBY became aware of the length of time the little girl had been standing there talking to him. There was no harm in it, of course, but . . . didn't parents warn their children about talking to strangers? Maybe he shouldn't encourage her to stay.

"Isn't it time you were going home for lunch?"

"I'm not hungry, so I don't think it can be time yet," Melanie said, moving to sit on the bottom step which led from the lane. Perhaps he wouldn't notice her there quite so much.

Toby watched her. He'd never had much to do with children, especially little girls. His sister had two boys and they certainly couldn't have been trusted to simply sit and watch.

Besides, this little girl's mother might be worrying.

"I think you'd better go home."

Melanie sighed. "It's not home. Home's not here. We came to look after Mummy's auntie. She fell.

"I only wanted to watch," she said sadly, getting to her feet to climb the steps.

Once in the lane she paused, twisting to look over her shoulder at him. "Can I come and see the wall when it's finished?"

"If you like," Toby agreed reluctantly. "But it might take quite a while to build it."

"I don't mind. There's nothing much to do in the country, is there?"

Toby watched her start off down the lane.

"Hey! What's your name?" he cried after her.

Melanie turned warily. "It's Melanie Linsey, and I'm six. I'm not a baby. I wouldn't have got in the way."

She began to walk away slowly, and after a moment Toby moved to the gateway.

"Melanie! I'll be starting this afternoon."

He looked back at the dark inviting hole and sighed. "Is it Mrs Cartmell you're staying with?" he asked, recalling hearing that the elderly woman had visitors. "Maybe I'd better speak to your mother."

Melanie's eyes widened.

"But I haven't done anything," she pleaded. "I was only watching — behind that bush, at first, but . . . I'm sorry I came into your garden without asking. I won't do it again. Promise!" she said in a rush.

Toby grinned, curbing the urge to reach out and ruffle the child's hair.

"I'm not angry. But if you are going to help me build that wall we'd better see if it's all right with your mother."

He watched the child's face light up expectantly.

"Can I really help? Really?" she asked.

"We'll see! But first I've got to see your mother, ask her to find you some old clothes, for a start."

PEGGY LINSEY hurried to open the kitchen door when she saw Melanie coming up the path with a young man.

"What's happened? Melanie hasn't been a nuisance, has she?"

"No!" The word came twice, in unison, once in an indignant tone, the other amused.

"No," Toby said again, his smiling eyes running over Peggy's embarrassed face.

"I'm Toby Stanton, by the way. And I've uncovered this old well," he said, nodding back towards the cottages. "In my garden. Melanie was . . . passing. I'm planning to build a low wall around it, partly to keep anyone from falling in, and also to make it ornamental. Melanie seemed interested."

"Oh, Melanie!" Peggy cried in dismay. "She's bored," she explained to Toby. "All the children here are back at school, but, luckily Melanie's term doesn't begin for another month. Luckily, because Mrs Cartmell, my aunt, had a bad fall."

"Yes, Melanie told me. There's nothing much to do in the country," he added.

Peggy chuckled ruefully.

"I do try to take her out when I can."

"Yes, she told me about your trip to the wishing well. She's hoping mine might have magic powers, but . . ."

He became aware that the smile had faded from the young woman's face and his words petered away.

"That wasn't now. I mean, we went on that trip before . . ." Peggy glanced down at her daughter and up into Toby's face. "And you mean you wouldn't mind if she came to watch you? That's very good of you. I expect she'll soon leave you in peace," she added hopefully.

"Maybe. But I don't intend to let her sit around and let me do all the hard work. What do you say, Melanie? Shall your mother look out your old clothes?"

"Oh, please, Mummy! And I'm sure it is a wishing well. It's so dark and mysterious. And because it's been there for hundreds of years with no-one knowing about it, must mean you're going to be extra lucky finding it like that. Don't you think, Mr Stanton?"

"We'll have to see. After lunch, then. And it's Toby." He smiled, and this time his hand did rest a moment on Melanie's blonde head, before he waved to her mother as he turned away.

Melanie and Toby had been working busily for some time when they heard footsteps on the flagged path.

"Could either of you two workers eat some buns? I've just finished baking," Peggy called. "There's lemonade, too, or coffee if you prefer it, Mr Stanton."

"Toby. And we'd love some buns, wouldn't we, Melanie?"

"Scrumptious!" Melanie exclaimed, taking the cake her mother proffered and going to sit on the bottom step.

"There's a chair somewhere around," he said, moving towards the shed which leant drunkenly against the cottage wall.

"I haven't been here very long and everything needs doing up," he said once they were all settled. "I suppose, really, I shouldn't be wasting time on the well."

"But we can't stop now," Melanie cried in horror. "Tell him, Mummy. We've got to finish the wall and make the well look nice. It must have been horrid being hidden under those great stones for ages and ages. You didn't really mean you'd stop, did you?"

"Of course not! Who cares if the house falls down and I have to live out in the garden?"

Melanie giggled. "When the well's ready you could wish for all the other jobs to be done for you."

"Now, why didn't *I* think of that? If that's the case, the sooner we get back to work, the better, young Melanie."

IT took several days for Toby and Melanie to build the wall round the well to their satisfaction, and Toby enjoyed the time almost as much as Melanie quite obviously did.

"Perhaps we should plant some flowers round the top," Toby said one afternoon, when the work was nearing completion. "And a well should have a bucket and some kind of winding mechanism. Don't you agree, Peggy?"

Melanie's mother turned from repacking the picnic basket she had brought down to the cottage each afternoon, after that first day.

"Perhaps. It's your well, Toby. But what about all those other jobs you planned to do?"

"They can wait. Anyway, it's *our* well, isn't it, Melanie?"

"Yes. And we've just got to finish it before we have to go home. I must have my wish. You said I could when we'd finished, Toby. You promised."

"And I meant to. I don't suppose it matters about the bucket, but I think there's time to do the flowers."

He took the picnic basket from Peggy's hand, walking beside her into the lane.

"When do you have to leave?"

"Melanie's school opens next week, but I'll need time to get everything ready. We ought to leave on Thursday."

"I'll miss . . . Melanie. She's a great kid. I've enjoyed these last few weeks. I'd certainly like to see her get her wish."

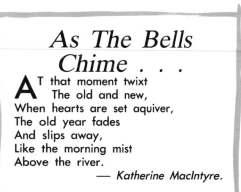

As The Bells Chime . . .

AT that moment twixt
The old and new,
When hearts are set aquiver,
The old year fades
And slips away,
Like the morning mist
Above the river.

— *Katherine MacIntyre.*

Two days later the well was finished. The wall rose, if a little wobbly in places, for about two feet, its top crowned by a bright ring of small creeping plants. Toby and Melanie were sitting, surveying their work with contented smiles, when Peggy arrived with the customary afternoon tea.

"Don't you think it looks good?" Toby asked, taking her hand to draw her closer.

"It does look like a wishing well," Melanie said consideringly.

"It looks smashing," Toby agreed. "I think we can be proud of ourselves."

He unscrewed the stopper from the bottle of lemonade Peggy had brought.

"This isn't champagne, but it'll have to do, I suppose. I think we ought to have a launching ceremony. I thought we ought to have a toast. Here, hand me your cups," Toby ordered. "We'll drink to friendship and to the future."

He raised his drink. "Here's to Toby and Melanie's wishing well. May it always grant everyone's wishes."

Solemnly Melanie raised her cup and drank.

"Is it really a wishing well, now? If I wish, will it come true?"

"Maybe," Toby nodded. "Of course it depends what you wish for.

I wouldn't make it anything fantastic, if I were you. You've got to remember, Melanie, love, that this is a pretty new wishing well. It might not have got the hang of things properly yet."

Peggy caught at his fingers squeezing them, glad of his understanding.

"Toby's right, love. Don't expect too much."

They waited, their fingers still entwined as Melanie went to stand by the low wall.

"I wish . . ." she began, then suddenly she was turning back to them. "I haven't got any money."

Smiling, Toby reached into his pocket, pulling out a handful of change and offering it to her.

Melanie looked at the coins, touching them thoughtfully.

"Do you mind if I take a silver one? I'll pay you back when I get my spending money. Daddy said, that time we went to that other wishing well, that as mine was only a small wish a penny should be enough. Do you remember, Mummy?"

"Yes, darling," Peggy said, and Toby felt her grip tighten.

"Here, take what you want," he said, thrusting his palm forward.

For several seconds Melanie's head remained bent over the coins, then her fingers plucked out the fifty pence piece.

'It is rather an important wish," she said somewhat apologetically.

They watched in silence as she went to lean on the low wall, but then she looked back at them again.

"It's an awful long way down. I can't even see the bottom," she said, her brow creased with concern. "At that other well, it wasn't deep, you could see all the coins. Perhaps the . . . well, whatever it is, won't hear me if I just whisper like I did then. You won't listen if I talk out loud, will you?"

"Of course not!" Toby tugged Peggy's hand, forcing her to turn away. "You go on and wish, young Melanie."

"I wish . . ." There was a slight gulp which Toby couldn't quite identify, but there was no mistaking Melanie's next words.

"I wish Toby could be my new daddy."

HE felt Peggy's fingers slide from his and heard her whisper the child's name.

Swiftly he faced her.

"It's all right, Peggy. She's only a child. She doesn't understand. Melanie, I told you not to wish for anything impossible."

"But it isn't impossible," Peggy said quietly, and as Toby continued to stare at her she turned away. But not before he had seen the way her cheeks were tinged with pink.

"I'm sorry, Toby. I must apologise for Melanie, but I thought you knew. I just took it you'd heard.

"I'm a widow, Toby. Melanie's father died almost four years ago. She barely remembers him."

Toby stood watching the light fade from her face, unable to take in what she had just told him.

She was free! She didn't belong to someone else. And if that expression he had seen on her face before she'd turned so quickly away was anything to go by, then maybe Melanie wasn't the only one who'd been hoping.

Suddenly, to Peggy and Melanie's surprise, he plunged his hand into his pocket and drew out the change once more. Stepping towards the child he poured the coins on to the wall.

"Here! Put them all in. Fifty pence is no fit price for such a wish. But take your time, Melanie. Your mummy and I have something to say to each other which might take a little while." □

PARTNERQUOTES ★ ★

VIVIEN LEIGH

1933: Savoy Grill, London, on seeing Olivier across the room, never having met him: *"That is the man I am going to marry."*

1938: Myron Selznick (brother of producer, David, of "Gone With The Wind" fame) introduced her to his brother thus: *"By the way, David, here's your Scarlett . . ."*
Later in life: *"I had Guy Fawkes Day for a birthday and so I always expected there would be fireworks in my life."*

LAURENCE OLIVIER

1930s: On not doing well filming with Garbo: *"Just give me my dough and I'll go."*
1967: On leaving Vivien, who had been mentally ill for some time: *"You can reach a point when it's like a life raft that can hold only so many. You cast away the hand grasping it because otherwise it's both of you . . ."*
1984: *"Acting is lying, and good acting is lying convincingly."*

LAURENCE OLIVIER & VIVIEN LEIGH — AN EXPLOSIVE LOVE

From This Day Forward

by JEAN MELVILLE

HOW ill her mother looked, Lorna Westcott thought, as she stood beside the hospital bed and stared at the tired white face under the large bandage on her head. What a thing to happen!

Mrs Newell had been hurrying to get off the bus near her home, her arms full of shopping from the January sales, when her foot slipped on the icy pavement. Nothing had broken her fall and she had cracked the back of her head on the hard pavement.

A neighbour had rushed to telephone Lorna about her mother's accident, but an ambulance had already been called and now, drowsy with drugs, Dorothy Newell lay in the local general hospital.

"Don't worry about a thing, Mum," Lorna whispered. "I'll see to the house."

"You've got your own house to think about," her mother whispered "And Sandy to look after."

"We'll both do all we can. Do you want anything? The nurse says I can't stay for long."

"I want Brenda," her mother said clearly. "It's time she came home."

Lorna's heart lurched. Her mother wanted Brenda, her elder sister . . .

"Write to her. Tell her to come," Mrs Newell whispered. "Promise."

"I . . . I promise," Lorna said, and left the ward with an uneasy heart.

"I've got to ask her to come home," Lorna explained to Sandy, her husband, when she returned home from the hospital.

"Mum wants her. She's had an awful crack on the head, Sandy, and she looks really ill. I've simply got to carry out her wishes."

Sandy's face lacked expression.

"Write to her by all means, Lorna. I don't mind. Of course she must come home. Philip, too, if he can get away from his job."

He drew a deep breath. "They can both stay here."

"They can stay at Mother's house," Lorna said sharply. "There's plenty of room while she's away."

What would it be like to have her sister home again, Lorna wondered the following morning as she cleared away the breakfast things. Was it only three years since Brenda and Philip had gone away? Sometimes it felt like a lifetime — and sometimes only yesterday.

Lorna watched her husband leave the house on his way to his job at the local bank. Sandy and her sister, Brenda, had been engaged to be married for two years and the wedding had been planned well ahead. Lorna was to be her sister's bridesmaid, and Sandy's great friend, Philip Davidson, was to be best man. Philip worked for an insurance company with offices above the bank and all four young people had been the best of friends.

Then, with just a week to go before the wedding, Brenda and Philip Davidson had run away. She had left a note for her parents and Lorna, as well as a letter to Sandy, but the whole family had been stunned by the news.

No-one had noticed the growing attraction which Brenda claimed she and Philip had felt for one another. He had the opportunity of a job in London and to avoid arguments, so Brenda explained, she and Philip were running away together. They were going to be married as soon as possible.

AFTERWARDS, the family had seen little of Sandy Westcott. Brenda's parents, Mr and Mrs Newell, had grown fond of him and had looked forward to welcoming him into the family.

Mr Newell's health was poor, and when he died a few months later, Sandy had come to the funeral and had offered his services

Joy Of My Heart

THERE'S a sea of cheerful wee faces,
   That appear to be smiling at me,
A'bobbing and waving and bowing
   And bumping each other with glee.

Freshly washed with the dew of the
      morning,
   The wind shaking their petals to dry,
Velvety red, white, purple and yellow
   And some as blue as the sky.

The plain Janes among the more vivid
   Plants picoted, frilled and so fancy,
But of all the plants in my garden,
   The joy of my heart is the pansy.
      — *Katherine MacIntyre.*

42

later in sorting out any financial matters. Lorna had been specially pleased to accept the offer, since most of this had fallen on her shoulders.

Brenda had made a hurried visit home for the funeral, but had left again early the following morning. It had not been a happy meeting between the sisters.

"Sandy was heartbroken," Lorna had said accusingly. "We all hated to see him so upset."

"He would have been even more upset if we'd had a broken marriage," Brenda returned.

"But are you happy with Philip Davidson?"

"Of course. I married him, didn't I?"

But there had been deep upset in Brenda, and Lorna had worried about it later. Was her sister having second thoughts? Did she regret losing Sandy?

She could well understand it if Brenda *was* regretting how things had turned out. As she got to know Sandy, Lorna began to admire him more than any man she had known. And to love him. She had fallen deeply in love and soon she and Sandy were constant companions.

When he asked her to marry him, she had looked at him searchingly.

"Are you *sure*, Sandy? After Brenda?"

"It's you I want, Lorna," he said quietly. "Brenda was right. It would have been a mistake. But I have fallen in love with you."

"And I love you, Sandy," she assured. "I do. So very much."

Mrs Newell had continued to live in the old family home, and Lorna and Sandy had found a house nearby. Gradually Lorna accepted that her only sister had now settled down in London and their lives became pleasant and happy.

They exchanged cards and gifts with Brenda and Philip at Christmas, and apart from her quick dash home to attend her father's funeral, Brenda had no desire to leave London. She was either busy or moving, or Philip had just been promoted and was very busy settling in.

It hurt Mrs Newell that her elder daughter seemed to be lost to her.

Mrs Newell had gone to the sales to buy new bed linen, hoping to entice Brenda and Philip to come home for Easter. But the visit would have to be now, in January, if she came at all, thought Lorna, as she penned the letter.

Suppose her sister did come home? She and Sandy had only met briefly at Mr Newell's funeral. This visit would be different. How would Sandy feel when he saw Brenda again? And Philip? Once they had been such good friends.

Lorna pushed aside her fears. If it re-opened old wounds for Sandy, if there was even the smallest rekindling of his love for her sister, how hurtful it was going to be.

Her love for Sandy had grown after marriage, but sometimes she saw a watchful look on his face when she talked about the other couple. He was still disturbed by them.

It was a bad fall, she wrote to her sister. *Mother injured the back of her head. She wants to see you, Brenda. If only you and Philip could get a few days off . . .*

She paused and bit her lip. *You can stay at home, or with Sandy and me, just as you wish.*

B RENDA rang briefly the following evening and said she and Philip would come. They would stay in her old home.

"Philip is coming with me," she said on the phone. "He is due to visit his own parents, anyway, so he's arranged to take a week of his holidays."

"Great," Lorna said.

"How . . . how is she?" Brenda asked, and the fear was plain in her voice.

"She doesn't look well, but she's no worse," Lorna said.

"We'll travel tomorrow," Brenda promised.

For a few days after Brenda and Philip arrived, Mrs Newell's condition remained the same and there was a great uneasiness between the young couples.

Brenda seemed more than usually worried about their mother, but Lorna wondered if this was a front, because she wanted to avoid talking about Sandy.

Sandy, too, had gone very quiet, and Lorna caught a look of anger on his face as she looked at Philip Davidson. Once they had been such friends. Now there was nothing but suspicion between them.

As the days passed and it was nearly time for the young couple to return to London, Lorna did manage to speak to her sister.

"Has Mother really improved?" Brenda asked. "You . . . you don't think there's any danger, do you?"

"The doctor says she has made good progress since you came."

"I'm so frightened in case she has a relapse and . . . and . . . I'll lose her, too."

"Don't talk nonsense like that!" Lorna said firmly.

"It's true."

Suddenly, Brenda was in tears and Lorna put her arms round her sister.

"Just like Dad," she whispered. "It was my fault, wasn't it? He was never ill until I . . . I ran away like that. I knew he was upset when he wrote to me. I gave him a shock when I ran away with Philip and it weakened his heart, then he took that attack. I . . . I was responsible."

"I've never heard such rubbish," Lorna said. "Is *that* what you've been thinking all this time? You weren't responsible for Dad. He retired early because of his health. He's been unwell for years, but of course, we were the last to be told. I heard Mum telling Sandy and got it out of them."

Brenda's tears began to lessen.

A Favourite Bay

OH, to be at a favourite bay
    Where Atlantic breakers roll,
There the silver spray,
Grasps sheer, grey cliffs,
Like claws, to reach it's goal.

To watch the gannets wheel and soar
Above the raging Corryvrekan
And hear the boom of the undertow
As each frothing wave's breakin'.

To stand alone at Kintyre's Mull
When the Rathlin light
Sweeps o'er the sea,
And sense the peace of God all
    around —
That's the place I long to be.
            — *Katherine MacIntyre.*

"Oh, Lorna, is that really true? I missed him such a lot but I can bear it if . . . if it wasn't my fault. That's why I wouldn't come home. I . . . I felt so awful."

"Well, that's over now. And Mum's getting better, too. She could be allowed home next week."

Brenda's voice began to brighten. "I'll have to tell Philip. He's been so worried about me. I think I'm expecting a baby. I'm going to tell Mum before I go home. If it's a boy, I'll call him Alistair, after Dad."

"That's marvellous news," said Lorna. "Then you're really happy with Philip?"

"We love each other," Brenda said simply. "We couldn't help it. Every time we all went out together, it got worse. We just had to be together. It seemed the only thing to do."

"I see," Lorna said. She was glad Brenda and Philip were so happy. But where did that leave Sandy?

THAT evening she cleared away the supper things, then drew a deep breath.

"I would like to invite Brenda and Philip for a celebration dinner here before they go home to London," she said. "Sandy . . . Brenda thinks there's a baby on the way."

Sandy laid his paper aside. He stared hard at her white face and the look of distress and anger was back in his eyes.

"Bully for Philip," he said. "He's sorting himself out very well."

Lorna's heart stabbed with pain. So Sandy *was* still hurt.

"Can't we make an effort to forget?" she asked huskily. "I thought you had got over it, Sandy. I thought we were happy, you and I."

"Oh, I got over Brenda quickly enough, but what about you? I know you cared about Philip. You were always with him when we all went out together, and you were so upset at the break up. I could see then that you had expected you and Philip . . . well . . ."

"There was *never* anything between Philip Davidson and me," she cried. "There was only ever you, Sandy. I liked Philip a lot, but not in that way. Surely you know that? I've told you often enough."

He stared into her face. "But you kept wondering about him . . . if he really loved Brenda. You've said so many times. And you keep watching him. Even during this visit, you've kept watching him."

"Only to see if he and Brenda were happy. And they are. At first she would tell me nothing, so I tried to guess by watching her and Philip together, but now I know. They are happy."

Sandy drew her into his arms.

"Then so are we," he said, as he kissed her. "So are we, because I love you more than I ever loved Brenda."

Lorna leaned against him. Her heart was at peace at last and her happiness was like the warmth of spring. She would make it very special for the four of them.

It would mark the beginning of their very own, very real, married happiness. □

Fate Takes A Hand

by ANNE MURRAY

IT was after she had completed her shopping in the supermarket that Mrs Manson paused in front of the next-door book shop, noticing that today someone had placed a long table outside it.

And on the table were simply piles of old books, all offered at the attractive price of twenty pence each.

Mrs Manson was well aware that there were already far too many books in her home. However, she did feel that if she gave herself the treat of buying just one more, it would be a little reward for having had to queue so long at the check-out in the store. It was all those people who wrote cheques . . .

She began looking over the books. Only in this sort of display did you ever see old friends from childhood days, she told herself, as she hesitated between copies of *The Wide Wide World* and *The Heir Of Redclyffe*.

Of course, both of these had been published many years before she was born, but she had vivid memories of visits to her grandmother — and the thrill of discovering a pile of Victorian books in the attic. How eagerly she had read through them!

She could remember shedding tears over the troubles of Ellen Montgomery in *The Wide Wide World*, yet she had never cared much for John, who was the hero and dearly loved by Ellen. John was really too good to be true . . .

Well, perhaps she would take *The Heir Of Redclyffe*. Extracting a coin from her purse in readiness, she picked up the book and glanced through the pages.

Oh, yes, in these pages she would find a few hours' real relaxation of the sort which doesn't come often to a busy housewife.

It was just as she was looking with interest at the cover picture of a young lady falling down a precipitous hillside, wearing the long skirts of Victorian days, that a sudden groan of brakes alerted her to the fact that the bus she wanted was just pulling up at the stop beyond the bookshop.

Oh dear, she simply must catch it. Her husband, Robert, would be home for lunch, and so would the two cousins who were staying with them this week, and who might have finished their morning of sightseeing by now.

Surely they wouldn't be waiting on the doorstep? That would never do.

Raising her hand to brush away a tiresome fly which buzzed in her face, Mrs Manson abandoned the books and hurried to join the queue surging towards the bus. Presently she was inside and even managed to get a seat.

The bus moved off and it was only after it had gone more than halfway to her stop that she became suddenly aware that she had never taken the book inside the shop and paid for it.

Nor had she put it back on the table . . .

A wave of colour swept up over her face and she half rose. The driver slowed down, then frowned at her as she resumed her seat.

"There just isn't time to go back now and pay for it," she told herself sensibly. "I'll go along after lunch."

She remained in her seat, outwardly calm, so that none of the other passengers could guess that in her heart there was the most uncomfortable feeling of guilt. To think that she — President of the Woman's Guild, only just retired from years of Sunday school teaching — could do a thing like that!

Even if only twenty pence was involved, it still wasn't right. Her thoughts were in confusion.

The Heir Of Redclyffe lay on her lap and no longer gave her any pleasure. Would she ever read it without remembering just how she had acquired it?

M RS MANSON was so worried, in fact, that after she had left the bus and was opening her own garden gate, it was hardly a surprise to discover that somewhere on the way home she must have dropped her purse.

It was certainly no longer in her hand where she had been holding it when she got on the bus. It wasn't in her jacket pocket, either, nor inside her shopping bag.

Really, she thought, what was the matter with her today, doing such stupid absent-minded things.

Glancing towards the house, she realised there was no time to search for the purse. More urgent problems lay ahead, for both her visitors were indeed hovering about the doorstep.

Worse still, there was Robert, striding up and down the lawn impatiently. Once again he must have mislaid his own key, but what had brought him home so early?

Robert greeted her reproachfully.

"Did you forget that I wanted lunch early?" he asked. "This is the afternoon I lecture at two o'clock to that American philosophical club."

▶ *over* ◂

══PARTNERQUOTES══

INGRID BERGMAN

1956: *"All right, I had a baby before I was married. It's not the first time that ever happened, and it's not the last . . . anyone can make a mistake. It's how they act after the mistake that they should be judged."*

1956: *"I probably loved him from the time I saw his first picture . . . he was alive and made me feel alive."*

1974: *"If you marry for the right reasons, for trust and understanding and love, then you cannot hate your husband or call him an idiot when the marriage is over . . ."*

1974: *"I'm not scared to stand up for the things I believe in. You can't be anything without courage."*

ROBERTO ROSSELLINI

1950: *"You and I will make beautiful movies together . . ."*

INGRID BERGMAN & ROBERTO ROSSELLINI — A LOVE THAT SHOCKED

Mrs Manson restrained herself from telling him this was the very first time she had heard of any lecture to Americans. Thankful that her own key was safely in her pocket, she unlocked the front door and everyone entered the house.

Her cousins followed her into the kitchen. Mildred and Jane were retired schoolteachers, energetic talkative women who had never married, and didn't seem to mind in the least.

It was a pity that their well-meant efforts to help were really more of a hindrance, but Mrs Manson tried to keep calm, and at length an adequate lunch was ready. She sighed with relief, especially as Robert seemed to have got over his earlier impatience and was now willing to chat to the visitors.

"Had you a look at the shops?" he asked Jane.

"Yes, indeed," she replied eagerly. "We country cousins do like your big stores where they put out such heaps of things on display."

"I'm sure these shops must lose a lot," Mildred remarked seriously. "It would be far too easy for a dishonest person to pop some little thing into a bag."

Mrs Manson felt her face grew hot again. Hurriedly she inquired what the two ladies thought of doing this afternoon.

"Helping you, dear, since we deserted you this morning," Mildred answered promptly. "There must be lots of things we could do for you."

For one wild moment Mrs Manson toyed with idea of asking them to polish the brass stair rods, keeping them busy that way while she slipped out to go to the book shop.

But no, they were such a kindly pair, who had worked hard all their lives and deserved a good holiday now. What about suggesting they each had a little rest while she herself popped out again to do just one quick errand?

"Oh, no, dear." Mildred laughed. "We haven't got to that stage yet. We'll go out with you."

Mrs Manson felt trapped. No way was she going to let them know how stupid she had been this morning. Perhaps she should just forget the whole thing — after all, what was twenty pence these days?

Yet her tiresome conscience wouldn't let her forget. Murmuring

▶ p52

SOME of Scotland's wildest scenery lies along Glen Torridon. Across Loch Clair are remnants of primeval Caledonian forest and prominent are the peaks of Liathach (3456 ft.) and Beinn Eighe (3188 ft.). The village of Torridon is to be found north of upper Loch Torridon. The mountains lining both sides of the valley are formed of red Torridon sandstone and the horizontal rock strata give the slopes a distinctive banded appearance. The National Trust for Scotland has a local visitor centre and a deer museum, and the area is part of a national nature reserve. Views from the mountains stretch to Cape Wrath and the Outer Hebrides.

TORRIDON, ROSS-SHIRE : J CAMPBELL KERR

something about not being ready yet, she went upstairs to the refuge of her bedroom for a few minutes' thought.

I'll just slip out by the back door, she decided.

But from her window she could see her cousins now strolling about the garden, finally settling themselves in the deck-chairs at the other side of the lawn. From there it would be possible to see anyone emerging from either the front or back door.

What was to be done now? But the sound of a creak broke into Mrs Manson's troubled thoughts. Someone was coming into the garden by the gate which needed oiling so badly.

Looking down, she saw the stalwart figure of a policeman coming up the path. Was it because of what she had done? Had she really been spotted? Perhaps too many people had been walking off with books without paying and it had been decided to put a check on it.

But how had they got on to her so quickly? Trembling a little, she went downstairs to the open front door.

G OOD afternoon, Mrs Manson," the policeman said, with quite a friendly smile.

He was, she realised, the one sometimes to be seen about this district, and more than once she had exchanged a word with him about the weather.

"Good . . . good afternoon," she answered weakly, wondering if all this would be reported in the local paper.

In her imagination she saw headlines: *Lecturer's Wife Fined.* Something like that. Robert would never recover from the disgrace.

"This'll be yours, I think," the policeman went on, holding out a small familiar article. "It was lying just a few yards from your gate, and I see your name's inside," he added approvingly. "It's lucky no-one else saw it."

"Oh, thank you! Thank you!" Mrs Manson cried, beyond caring what he thought of her enthusiastic gratitude for the return of a battered old purse containing only a few coins.

She longed to tell him she was really grateful for the discovery that he hadn't come to arrest her, but there was no point in doing so — especially as she could see Mildred gazing at them curiously, trying to hear what was said.

After a short friendly conversation about the good weather, the policeman went away. Mrs Manson hurried indoors to get her bus pass. She would wait no longer.

She simply must put an end to this state of affairs when a simple incident could throw her into needless panic.

"Wait, dear, I'll come with you," Mildred called as she saw her hostess hasten down the path.

But it took time to get out of that very low deck-chair, and Mrs Manson saw with relief that a bus was in sight and she would be on it before Mildred could catch up.

Well, when she returned she would make it up in some way to her guests for this abrupt desertion of them. But first of all she had to make her confession at the book shop, and as the bus rolled on she felt rather as she did when visiting the dentist.

At last she was there, noticing in passing that *The Wide, Wide World* still lay on the table. She went inside, advancing nervously to the counter, where a young man came forward to serve her.

He smiled to her exactly as though he recognised her, but that didn't seem possible. Before he could speak she started bravely on her explanation.

"Oh, when I was here this morning I took a book from the table by the door . . . it was twenty pence." she got out.

"Yes, that's right," the young man said, in the tone of one who knew all about the matter.

He turned and lifted some coins from a ledge on which they seemed to have been laid aside. Handing them to her, he continued:

"I thought you might come back to get your change."

Mrs Manson stared at him in bewilderment, wondering if all this was just a strange dream. What on earth did he mean?

He gave her another cheerful grin.

"You caught your bus anyway!" he said. "A good thing I could see you through the window, so when you waved I knew to go out and lift your money off the table before anyone else picked it up."

Mrs Manson was just about to deny ever waving or leaving money when she recollected how she had put up her hand to brush away that fly. The coin she had been holding must have slipped from her grasp then landed on the table. And it hadn't been a twenty pence piece but one of these pounds which she had made mistakes with on previous occasions.

Was that it? It must be!

So had all her anxiety, her guilty fears, been quite unnecessary? Had she really been worried for no reason at all? Mrs Manson suddenly began to feel sorry for herself.

She felt it was essential that in some way she made up to herself without delay. And all at once she knew what she was going to do.

Holding out one of the twenty pence coins she had just been given in change, she told the pleasant young man she would now also buy that copy of *The Wide, Wide World.* □

THE Farne Islands overleaf are a collection of 15 or so islands of bare, rock lying between two and five miles off the Northumberland coast. They form a noted wildlife sanctuary. Largest and nearest to the mainland is Farne Island, its 16th-century tower built by Prior Castell of Durham, now converted into the headquarters of the Farne Islands Bird Observatory. Grace Darling became the heroine of the islands at the age of twenty-three when she rowed out with her father, the keeper of the Longstone Lighthouse in the Farne Islands, to rescue five people from a wrecked steamer, in 1838. Her boat is in a Bamburgh museum.

FARNE ISLANDS LIGHTHOUSE : J CAMPBELL KERR

A S Karen Reynolds walked briskly across the school playground, young Barry Stoker darted out of the door, head down. He didn't see her until he almost collided with her. Then he looked up, startled.

"Hello, Barry. How's Dad today?"

Without replying, the lad raced away towards the gate.

Karen glanced after him, puzzled. It wasn't like Barry to be so unfriendly, and it certainly was odd for him to be leaving school so soon after the final bell rang. Usually he lingered, helping his teacher with the classroom pets, or any little job that needed doing.

Karen would liked to have known how Ken Stoker was. She had heard that her neighbour had suffered another set-back on the long road to recovery from his serious illness of a year ago.

It had been tough for the Stoker family, and Barry's mother had a lot to cope with, looking after her four chidren as well as a sick husband. Eileen Stoker had always helped Karen, when as a new widow with a little daughter, she had come to live next door.

No-one could have been a better support and friend in those difficult times and it distressed Karen to see how these good people had to struggle now.

Most of the children at Bank Street School greeted Karen by name as she passed on her way to collect her cleaning equipment from the caretaker's room. Everyone felt that they were a member of a big, happy family — from the headmaster, Mr Beazly, to Karen, the cleaner. It was the nicest thing about this school.

Shortage of money had forced Karen to take on the job after her husband had died, and Eileen Stoker had been only too glad to care for baby Milly for the few hours night and morning that she was needed.

Once Milly had started school, Karen had been able to take on extra work at Mrs Cotter's wool shop, but her

A New Life

Calls...
by JEAN MURRIE

fondness for the folk at the school made her reluctant to relinquish her first job. Their friendship was of even more value than the few pounds she could earn.

As she walked past Barry's class, she noticed that, unusually for this time of day, the room was empty. Paul Donaldson, the teacher, must have gone home early. Perhaps that's why Barry had dashed off.

Further down the corridor, she saw that Laura Stanley, the reception class teacher, was missing also — not surprising as Paul always gave her a lift home. But Milly was waiting for her there, quietly colouring in a picture.

Karen frowned, a little disconcerted that her daughter should be left unattended. Normally, Milly went home with Barry, but during the present crisis, Karen felt it unfair to burden Eileen with any more responsibility.

Milly correctly interpreted the cause for concern on her mother's face.

"It's all right. Mr Beazly is keeping an eye on me," she reassured. "Look. I'm doing this picture for Miss Stanley. D'you think she'll like it?"

"Sure to, dear," Karen responded as enthusiastically as she could but felt an unreasonable stab of jealousy.

She had prepared herself for Milly's entry into the world of school and was aware that because the two of them had been so close, her daughter's natural attachment to her teacher would cause a little pain. However, the resentment she felt for Laura Stanley was quite unreasonable.

The vivacious red-haired teacher couldn't be that much younger than herself, but Karen felt that she was years older, her youth gone with the responsibilities of motherhood.

A S usual, she prepared to start work on Paul's classroom first. He made his class tidy up well so it wouldn't take long to do. However, today there was a considerable amount of litter under the row of cages and tanks along one wall.

The tame rats, gerbils and hamsters all needed care at the weekends and holidays, and Karen and Milly had been quite happy during those times to slip in from their nearby home to tend them.

It was next to impossible to keep any kind of pet in their cramped

▶ *p60*

B UILT between 1883 and 1890, the Forth Railway Bridge is one of the finest examples of engineering in the world. It is 2765 yards long and 361 feet above the water. Five thousand workmen were employed in the building of the bridge, which was designed by Sir John Fowler and Sir Benjamin Baker. The bridge featured in John Buchan's classic thriller, "The Thirty-Nine Steps," with hero Richard Hannay fleeing from the police and trying to unravel the mystery of the "Steps."

FORTH RAIL BRIDGE : J CAMPBELL KERR

flat so Paul Donaldson's menagerie made a good substitute. It was through casual discussion over the animals' welfare that something of a bond had grown up between the tall, good-looking teacher and herself.

And more recently, they shared a mutual concern over Barry, and his occasionally difficult behaviour.

"I don't want you to tell tales out of school." Paul had grinned wryly at the awful pun. "But I feel that things at home aren't too good and I know you're on friendly terms with his mother. Is there anything you can tell me which would explain his moods and awkwardness?"

So Karen told him about Ken Stoker's frequent hospital visits and how distracted and burdened Eileen was.

"Being the eldest, Barry has an awful lot of things to do at home just now," she said. "And of course, he's worried, too."

Paul had looked at her closely then and Karen had shifted uneasily under his interested gaze.

She didn't feel at her best in her overall and sensible working shoes, unaware that Paul was considering a very pretty girl, flushed cheeks framed by wisps of curling hair, her large grey eyes troubled over Barry, although he knew that she had plenty of problems of her own.

Paul had learned something of her sad background since he had come to teach at the school and suddenly he wanted to know more about this sensitive, caring young woman.

"Mrs Stoker isn't the only one with worries. You've had more than your fair share, haven't you?" he probed gently.

Karen didn't talk freely about her past, sensing that the facts often created a barrier of embarrassment. But the genuine sympathy in Paul's face urged her to unburden herself.

"My husband was drowned while we were on holiday," she told him simply. "He decided to walk across the sands, but the tide cut him off. He was not a good swimmer."

Loyalty to her husband of little more than a year prevented her from adding that the unguided excursion across the estuary was typical of his foolhardy self. Nor could she speak of the anguish, as holding her baby daughter, she had waited for him on the beach, and of the dark days that followed as she started to build a life for herself and Milly.

Pride, misplaced perhaps, had prevented her running home to her parents. After all, she had defied their wishes by leaving school at seventeen in order to marry Lewis.

"But fate and friends have been good, and we've managed fine, Milly and I."

The defiant lift of her chin was not lost on Paul and he smiled at her warmly.

"You've done a grand job," he said. "Milly's one of Laura's star pupils!"

It seemed to Karen that there was a subtle change in her relationship with Paul after this conversation. They became more than just employees in the same place, and she often sensed that Paul was looking out for her as she came on duty.

Yet she hesistated in letting her heart become involved too readily. Life was so complicated as it was, and there was the question of Laura. Karen felt sure that somehow she had a place in his scheme of things!

If ever there was a girl truly in love, there was one. Laura Stanley positively glowed as she moved about the school, especially radiant in Paul's presence.

K AREN gave herself a mental shake as she efficiently wielded her broom. It was no use going over the same ground, tormenting herself when her energies were needed elsewhere.

She swept up the chaff and seeds under the cages and as she straightened noticed that the cage of Sammy, the hamster, was open and the pet was gone. A hasty search of the immediate environment proved fruitless.

Looking for the hamster made her late. She still had the hall to sweep. Tomorrow, she would have to spend a little more time on it since the school was holding its annual disco in aid of school funds.

Before she and Milly returned home for tea, they had another quick look for Sammy.

"Leave a little dish of food for him near his cage," Milly pleaded, upset. "He might just return."

Next morning, Karen was determined to have a word with Barry before school started but he didn't appear.

"I left Barry sharpening pencils yesterday afternoon," Paul told her with a frown when he discovered what had happened. "Laura and I had to go to the Cash and Carry for balloons and streamers, so we left school promptly.

"I know that Barry can be a bit wayward at times, but I'd be surprised if he let the hamster go. No doubt we'll find out what transpired when he eventually turns up."

It was a day for Karen to help in the wool shop. Mrs Cotter was trying to expand the business by trying out new lines, and school affairs were pushed firmly to the back of Karen's mind as she helped to unpack a consignment of children's clothes.

When her busy hours there were over, she hurried back to school to meet Milly and begin work on the hall. A merry scene was taking place in Paul's room as some of his pupils blew up balloons. Milly joined in the fun as Karen continued on her way. Paul slipped out after her.

"Barry was very late this morning," he told her. "He denies all knowledge of the hamster, but frankly I don't believe him. In fact, he's been in an awful mood all day. Couldn't even persuade him to stay behind with the others — not like him to miss out on any high jinks!

"He even says he's not going to the disco, though he paid for his ticket weeks ago. In fact he was one of the first to do so."

"Perhaps he wants to be at home when his mother returns from visiting the hospital. Oh, I do hope his father isn't worse. I should have called round to see Eileen today."

Paul stretched out a hand and lightly brushed her forehead as if to smooth away the lines of worry gathering there.

"You do enough already," he admonished gently. "You need cheering up. I hope you're coming to the disco — it's certainly not the most scintillating event in town, but good fun."

"Yes, I'll be there," she promised with a smile, her wayward heart beating that little bit faster at Paul's interest.

She edged away reluctantly. "But I'd better get a move on with the hall!"

S HE almost skipped down the corridor, but her joy was short-lived at the sight of a small figure by the PE benches, tears trickling down his cheeks.

"It's my fault," Barry whimpered. "I let him go. He bit me and I dropped him. I've looked everywhere for him."

Sliding on to the bench, Karen put an arm round the sobbing boy and hugged him to her.

"Sammy, you mean? I expect he bit you because he doesn't like to be woken up. Hamsters are night-time creatures."

"I know. But I just wanted to cuddle him. Now he's gone. I expect he's dead."

The crying increased, and Karen held him close until he was calmer, knowing that the tears were not for Sammy alone, but were an expression of all the pent-up worry over his parents.

Barry hastily wiped the sleeve of his jumper over his eyes as Paul, Laura and Milly, arms full of balloons, laughingly burst into the hall.

If Paul was surprised by the sight of the tear-streaked face before him, he didn't show it.

"Off you go home and change, Barry, or you'll be late for the disco," he said briskly, inviting no argument.

Barry scowled. "Stupid discos! Just for cissies. I'm not coming!"

Karen watched him sadly as he slunk out, hands in pockets, scuffing his dirty trainers against the floor as he went.

At once she knew what was really wrong. Barry had no suitable clothes for the disco. In all her anxiety, his mother had forgotten to rig him out in new shirt and jeans as she had planned.

She recalled that Eileen was one of the customers who had enquired about the possibility of Mrs Cotton stocking clothes for youngsters.

"I haven't the time to travel into town," she'd said. "So to buy locally would be really useful."

"Could we borrow some for him, do you think?" Paul wondered when Karen shared his concern.

"Pride," Karen said. "He wouldn't like it. I'm sure his mother has just forgotten and Barry wouldn't want to bother her about it. But I have an idea. P'raps we can do something. Can I use the phone?"

In a few minutes, it was all arranged. Karen would pick up the key to the shop from Mrs Cotter, choose an outfit, and Eileen would settle up when she could.

"I'll run you there," Paul offered. "It will save time."

Karen glanced quickly at Laura, but the girl seemed quite happy to get on with decorating the hall.

"Milly and I will manage fine," she said brightly, and her daughter nodded enthusiastically, pleased to be left with her beloved teacher.

It was an oddly intimate occasion as Karen and Paul dithered over the rack of boys' clothes in Mrs Cotter's shop.

"I'm a terrible shopper," Paul confessed. "I just grab the first thing that fits and have to live with my mistakes for ever, while my brother takes ages to make up his mind. You'd never think we were twins!"

Standing so close to him, Karen wanted to touch him, assure him that he always looked fine to her. Instead, she concentrated firmly on Barry's needs and in minutes they were on their way back to school with the new rigout.

Collecting Milly, she delivered the clothes to the Stoker house where the children were being cared for by Eileen's sister.

"Wow, thanks!" Barry's eyes gleamed as he took the clothes from her and she knew that her intuition had been right.

YOU look pretty, Mummy," Milly said later, when ready for bed, she waited for the baby-sitter to arrive. "I wish I was going to the disco, too."

"Your turn will come." Karen laughed, warmed by her daughter's praise.

It was only a school event, but she had put on her most glamorous dress and brushed her hair till it shone. She was determined to enjoy herself and now that Milly was at school and less dependent on her, perhaps she would be able to go out more.

It certainly wasn't the most sophisticated date on the calendar Karen thought with amusement, ears assailed with thumping music as she arrived. Barry was already there, knees and elbows going twenty to the dozen.

He grinned at her and jerked his thumbs ceilingwards. Perhaps his Dad was feeling better! Then she caught sight of Paul and Laura dancing close together, out of step but not noticing, absorbed in each other.

Karen's buoyant mood vanished at once. But as the pair dreamily swung round, she saw that the man wasn't Paul at all, just his double.

Paul was under a trestle table, unpacking yet another crate of lemonade.

"This lot would drink the Atlantic dry," he grumbled good-humouredly. He smiled at Karen appreciatively as he straightened up. "If you can lend a hand dispensing this, I'll all the sooner be free to shuffle a few bars with you."

"I presume that handsome man with Laura is your twin brother,"

63

Karen said with a joyous laugh, reaching for the plastic cups.

"Yes, and Laura has been crazy about him ever since she met him at a barbecue at our house last year."

Paul raised his eyes ceilingwards in mock despair.

"She's shadowed me ever since — hoping something of her beloved Neil's aura had rubbed off on me, I suppose!"

He deftly poured lemonade into the waiting cups.

"And how glad I am that at long last he realises he is just as crazy about her! Well, he must be mad to come to this thrash when he doesn't have to!"

"I'm enjoying it," Karen told him truthfully, her eyes glowing with deep happiness.

"So am I, absolutely," Paul replied, dropping his bantering tone. He pulled her towards him, and Karen experienced the delicious sensation of allowing her carefully-controlled feelings to flow free, her expression telling him all.

Their tender mood was abruptly shattered by shrieks from the corridor rising above the blare of music.

"A mouse! There's a mouse!" Girls enjoying being frightened scampered into the hall.

"It's only Sammy!" Barry scuttled in after them, treasuring something cupped in his hands.

He gave a triumphant laugh as he confronted Paul and Karen.

"He was running around the cloakroom, sir! He wanted to come to the disco, too, didn't he?"

Paul beamed. " 'Course! All the best souls come to the Bank Street School Disco, eh, Barry? But I think you should pop along to the classroom and return Sammy to his cage. I expect he would like a snooze after all his adventures!"

As Barry disappeared, followed by a now admiring retinue of classmates, Karen sighed contentedly.

"Oh, I'm so glad."

Paul regarded her quizzically. "What, about the hamster?"

"Yes. And about Barry, too. He's so much happier now. Everything seems to have worked out well for him."

"You had more than a little to do with that," he said tenderly. "Caring, perceptive person that you are!"

Confused, Karen didn't know how to answer, but willingly slipped into his arms as he pulled her towards the centre of the hall.

"I don't think this is supposed to be a polka!" she objected with a laugh as they were jostled by gyrating bodies.

"Who cares?" Paul cheerfully shouted above the din. "Anything goes. Do you come here often?"

She looked at familiar surroundings, wall bars and window ladders festooned with balloons and streamers, and chuckled.

"About twice a day!"

"Good. Might see you around then."

And as he lovingly laid his cheek against hers, Karen had not the slightest doubt that he would. ☐

by
**CATHIE
MITCHELL**

When Love Is All

BILL poked his head through the open doorway of the spare
bedroom and saw Anne on her knees, picking bits of fluff off
the new carpet.

"You still at it!" he exclaimed. "Good heavens, Anne, how often
are you going to go over this room?"

Anne sat back on her heels, brushed aside a wisp of dark hair that
fell across her forehead and focused her brown eyes resolutely on her
husband.

E

"I want it to be really nice for Mum," she said determinedly.

"It's perfect now! Really, Anne, it's all very well being house-proud, but it shouldn't become an obsession."

Anne tossed her head defiantly.

"It's the way I was brought up," she asserted. "And I'm not ashamed of it. I want Mum to see that I haven't forgotten everything she taught me."

"Let's not get into that old argument now." Bill sighed. "The point is, aren't you overdoing things just a bit? After all, Mum isn't exactly an invalid — quite the opposite, in fact.

"Besides." He paused, a frown creasing his handsome features. "She still hasn't agreed to come yet, has she?"

Anne got to her feet, fiddled with the new lace curtains for the umpteenth time then turned to Bill.

"She will," she said, putting more conviction into the words than she actually felt. "I told her it had to be decided this coming Saturday. And Mum knows I mean what I say."

Bill entered the room slowly, his gaze wandering over the new duvet, the pretty pink floral wallpaper he had put up.

"Maybe you shouldn't push her too hard," he began. "After all, it's not as if she's unhappy in that little flat. And what about her friends? From what I can gather her place is a kind of halfway house for most of the pensioners in the block."

Anne swung on him in a kind of triumph.

"Exactly! Mum's far too old to be playing host to so many. It's too much for her. If you ask me, I think a lot of them are just taking advantage of her soft nature."

Bill met her gaze evenly.

"Your mum is a very kind, caring person, Anne. That's not quite the same as being soft. No-one will take advantage of her. She can be just as determined as her daughter when she likes."

Anne jerked her shoulders, but the flush of resentment vanished as quickly as it came. She moved closer to Bill, her eyes clouding.

"I am only thinking of her," she murmured urgently. "I just want what's best for Mum."

"And you think coming to live with us is best for her?"

Anne arched her eyebrows.

"Of course! Why else would I suggest it? Her friends can come and visit her here as often as they like. I won't mind. Or I can take her to see them. She isn't going to be cut off from them, for goodness' sake."

"But will it be quite the same for her?"

Anne stopped short and waved her arms in a kind of exasperation.

"We've gone over this a dozen times," she declared sharply. "You've seen her place, you know what it's like. Paintwork faded or chipped, the wallpaper curling up at the corners, and as for that kitchen!"

"I've offered to redecorate it," Bill cut in. "But you've heard her.

Just refuses to let me. As I said, you're alike that way, both stubborn."

"It's not stubbornness," Anne flashed back at him. "It's just that she knows how busy you are, and feels it would be a terrible imposition on you. That's Mum all over, putting everyone else before herself."

A lump rose quickly in Anne's throat and her voice broke. When she looked again at Bill, her eyes were filling with tears.

"She's worked hard all her life, Bill. And she felt Dad's death a lot more than she ever let on. I simply think that at her age she should be taking things easy. She's entitled to it. And I owe her that much. I want to look after her, pamper her even."

Bill smiled gently and moved quickly to put his arms around her. He kissed her cheek.

"All right, dear," he murmured. "I understand. You don't have to convince me. So long as both of you are happy. You bring her here, if that's what she wants."

A S always, her quick temper melted under Bill's gentle nature and she was filled with the inevitable sense of remorse at having been sharp with him.

She resisted telling him that what her mum wanted did not figure too highly in her list of priorities and duties. Anne wasn't even sure if her mum knew what was best for herself! After four years in the pensioner's flat, it was obvious that even such a small place was becoming too much. Look how the place had deteriorated in that time!

Of course there had been the inevitable rows. She had expected that.

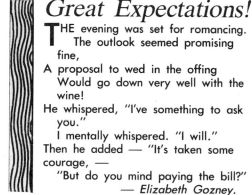

Great Expectations!

THE evening was set for romancing.
 The outlook seemed promising fine,
A proposal to wed in the offing
 Would go down very well with the wine!
He whispered, "I've something to ask you."
 I mentally whispered. "I will."
Then he added — "It's taken some courage, —
 "But do you mind paying the bill?"
 — *Elizabeth Gozney.*

old people could be obstinate and difficult at times, but Anne had made up her mind and, as Bill rightly said, she could be every bit as determined as her mum.

She hadn't expected an easy or early agreement from her mother. Anne knew her too well for that. So she had worked on her at every visit, pointing out the general untidiness of the place, and, worst of all, its sadly dilapidated decor.

At first Anne had thought her mum had simply lost interest, perhaps as a result of her father's death, as such indifference was so unlike her. And she was pleased, if not surprised, at how quickly she had established friendships with other pensioners in the building.

But this had not changed her attitude about the flat. She seemed to have lost all her old pride in good housekeeping, not that she had become slovenly. It was just a kind of carelessness, almost an indifference to things around her.

Of course, the fact that others were in and out the flat all day didn't help. Tidying up after so many visitors was bound to be tiring. It was small wonder she appeared to have given up trying.

On her regular tidying-up sprees, Anne had found a whole assortment of objects left by one or other of the pensioners. A magazine jammed behind the settee, a large knitting needle pushed into a cushion — she'd even found a grubby old pipe on the mantelpiece once.

She could remember her mum laughing at that.

"That's Peter's," she explained. "Must have left it yesterday. He's probably hunting high and low for it right now. He's getting so absent-minded these days."

Those words had sown the seed of an idea in Anne's mind, a seed that had grown steadily. Probably that was when she had really started worrying about her mum. Was *she* getting absent-minded? Forgetful?

There were no real signs of it, just this tendency to treat some of her valuable little ornaments as if they were of little account. She was mobile enough, active, and blessed with good health generally.

Of course, she wasn't exactly ancient, but then she was no youngster either.

As she drove to her mum's on the Saturday, Anne rehearsed what she would say and steeled herself to win the day.

TWO young men in white overalls were just finishing loading an assortment of tools into a small van parked just outside the ground-floor flat. Anne pulled in behind them and as they drove off, she moved forward to fill the space.

The first thing she noticed when her mum opened the door, was the strong smell of paint.

"Hello, dear." Her mum was her usual warm self, always so happy to see her daughter.

Anne felt a twinge of guilt at what was about to come, but for the moment, her carefully-prepared assault plans were forgotten as she gaped round the narrow hallway. The paintwork was gleaming white and the walls covered in a thick, soft-toned paper.

"Be careful of the paint, dear. It's still wet." The older woman smiled as they kissed, then turned to lead the way into her living-room.

Anne stopped in the doorway and felt her jaw drop in astonishment. It was completely transformed. The walls painted a warm, deep cream, the woodwork brilliant white.

"How do you like it, dear?"

At last, Anne managed to speak.

"It — it's lovely,"

"The kitchen's painted as well. Take a look."

Anne looked and discovered how true this was. The kitchen was as bright and sparkling as it had been on that first day when she and her mum had come to inspect the flat.

"Who did all this?"

"Charlie and Walter. They've only just left. Perhaps you saw them . . . ?"

"Two young chaps? In a small van?"

"That's them. They're Peter's boys. Painters to trade, you know." She threw that bit in to impress Anne. "Made a grand job, didn't they?"

Anne sank into a chair. Alarm bells started ringing in her head and she looked sharply at her mum.

"You did this deliberately, didn't you? Because of what I said about the place. How could you, Mum? To spend what little savings you have, too!"

Her mum chuckled merrily and Anne had the uncomfortable feeling that she *was* enjoying watching her daughter's astonished expressions.

"Didn't cost me a penny. I told you, they're Peter's sons. He got them to do it."

"Peter?" Anne repeated the name blankly, then remembered

▶ *over*

PARTNERQUOTES

JUDY

1939: *"I wouldn't be a big, grown-up star for anything. It's a million times more fun being just what I am."*
1951: *"I'm scared. Films have made me terrified of live audiences."*
"I'm a very emotional person. I love a good cry. But in my life there have been too many tears . . ."
1962: *"At twelve I was 'discovered' and taken to Hollywood, and suddenly, the fun stopped, and childhood was over."*

MICKEY

1965: *"Had I been brighter, had the ladies been gentler, had the Scotch been weaker, had the Gods been kinder, had the dice been hotter, this could have been a one-line story: Once upon a time, Mickey Rooney lived happily ever after . . ."*

JUDY GARLAND & MICKEY ROONEY — THE FAMOUS SCREEN KIDS

the old pipe she had found on the mantelpiece. "Oh, THAT Peter! Lives two doors along?"

"Yes. You've met him."

"Have I . . . ?" Anne sought to put substance to the name. She recalled an elderly man, very tall and erect for his age, who always had a pipe in his mouth.

"Peter has pestered me for months to let him have his sons come and redecorate the place," Her mum was chatting on, like some radio commentator giving a potted history. "Of course I told him not to bother.

"After all, it wasn't really necessary. I wasn't worried about it, so why should he be? But when you mentioned it, well, that's when I really saw how bad the flat had become.

"When I told Peter you felt that I couldn't look after the place properly, well, you wouldn't believe how he reacted. You'd have thought he was going to burst a blood vessel, his face got so red!

"And normally he's so quiet, firm, but gentle — rather like your father was."

"Anyway, he got so worked up, he picked up my phone and called his two sons to tell them he wanted this place completely redecorated before the weekend. I just didn't know what to say. And I couldn't turn those two nice boys away when they arrived at the door, could I?"

As she listened to her racing on, Anne found herself nodding or shaking her head in a kind of numb agreement. She felt a kind of resentment building inside her.

How dare this Peter fellow do this! What gave him the right to interfere? He was taking an awful lot on himself!

Anne straightened in her chair and struck a resolute pose.

"It was very nice of Peter, I'm sure. And the place really does look good. But that's not the point, is it?"

"Point?" Her mum looked baffled. "I don't understand, dear. What point?"

Anne made an effort to stifle her impatience.

"The point, Mum, is that we have prepared the spare room for you, and I'm sure you'll like it. Bill even bought a portable TV so you can sit there on your own if you want to —"

"I haven't time to watch TV," her mum interrupted sharply, waving at the old set in the corner. "I've hardly looked at that one. I told you at the time it was a waste of money buying it. I said I didn't want it!"

ANNE had an awful feeling that the discussion was not going her way, the way she had planned. She was on the defensive — not her mum! Of course the redecoration of the flat had caught her off guard, and had given a points victory to her mum.

But there were other factors to be taken into account, just as important as the flat's decor, perhaps even more important. And she was about to launch into these when the door bell chimed.

She heard a murmur of voices from the hallway, then her mum returned with Peter. Anne recognised the old pipe which, for once, wasn't in his mouth, but in his hand.

"You know my daughter, Anne." Mum smiled proudly at her. "Peter has just come to see if the boys have made a proper job."

Peter gave Anne a brief nod before turning to survey the room with a keen, perceptive eye. When he faced them again, he seemed satisfied.

"Not bad," he muttered. "Not bad at all, Marion."

"What do you mean, not bad?" Anne was startled at how vigorously her mum slapped Peter on the shoulder. "They've made a great job of it! Anne and I were just saying so, weren't we, Anne?"

Anne nodded, took a deep breath and was about to tactfully announce that she wanted to speak privately with her mother, when the front bell chimed again.

"That'll be Peggy," the lady of the house said.

Peggy was a small, thin woman, whom Anne vaguely recalled having seen from time to time. Her dark eyes seemed even larger than usual, and they were shining with excitement as they surveyed the room.

"Oh, it's just lovely, Marion," she declared breathlessly before turning her burning gaze on Anne. "Isn't your mum's flat just lovely, my dear?"

Again Anne acknowledged the remark with a dazed nod, her own eyes fixed on the large plate Peggy was holding in both spindly hands. Her curiosity was satisfied when her mum pulled away the little napkin draped over the plate to reveal a large cake topped with rich icing.

"What a beautiful cake!" Anne's mum exclaimed. She kissed Peggy on the cheek, took the plate from her and laid it on the table before turning proudly to her daughter. "Peggy made this cake herself. Wasn't that clever of her?"

Peggy waved a hand almost embarrassedly.

"Your mum taught me how," she declared. "Before she came all I could make was a simple omelette!" She giggled as she settled on the couch beside Anne. "A wonderful person, your mother," she whispered confidingly. "But you know that, of course.

"I'll tell you something, though, dear. Do you know I'd never been in any of the other senior citizens' houses until your mother came here? In fact, hardly any of us spoke much to each other. Kept mostly to ourselves in our own little flats. But Marion changed all that!"

She pointed a long thin finger at Anne's mum, who was talking to Peter.

"Wonderful woman she is, wonderful." She laughed happily and patted Anne's knee. "Her house is a positive haven. Don't know what some of us would do without her."

It's a conspiracy, Anne thought, trying to regroup her thoughts. It was a deliberate attempt to gang up on her. They were all involved, but it had probably been organised by her mum!

It was obviously a ploy to make her think again about trying to persuade her mother to give up her flat and come to live with her. It was intended to make her feel awful, feel guilty even . . . the trouble was, it was succeeding!

THE final crunch came when six other pensioners arrived, each bringing some little contribution to the get-together.

Anne watched in helpless silence as the women prepared tea, set out cups and saucers, cut the cake and chattered nonstop. Peter and another elderly man huddled in a corner, both sucking pipes and talking about some war or other.

The little room had become a positive hive of noise and activity, but, above all, it throbbed with obvious pleasure and life.

Now and again, one of the pensioners broke away from the others and came to chat to Anne, and they all told her the same story.

What a wonderful woman her mother was. How her home had become a focal point for all of them. But the biggest shock was learning that the get-together was as much a surprise to her mum as it was to Anne.

The others had planned it as a surprise, to celebrate the redecoration of the flat, and to say thanks to Marion.

Anne was close to tears when they began leaving. A deep pride surged inside her as she watched each of them kiss her mother, warmly, affectionately, as they left. There was no show or pretence in their open affection.

They were all at the age when little social courtesies had become meaningless, and direct honesty was everything. It was so obvious that for them her mother and her little flat had become a focal point, a meeting place that was not only welcoming, but important to them.

When the last guest had gone, Marion flopped gratefully into a chair, looking tired, but still glowing from an inner warmth and happiness.

Anne had been amazed at how quickly the women had cleared away the used cups and saucers, washed them and kept Anne from even getting close to the kitchen sink!

She studied her mother affectionately.

"You don't have many get-togethers like that, do you?"

Her mother chuckled.

"Goodness me, no, dear! Just on special occasions — somebody's birthday, or something like that. Usually we just sit around having a little chat. The women normally bring their knitting."

Anne almost laughed at her own sense of relief.

"Thank goodness for that. Soon wear you out if you did that too often. I certainly couldn't keep up with the pace. I'd be worn out!"

They lapsed into silence for a bit. Anne was quite happy to sit there, quietly content with just being close to her mum, and seeing her so happy. And she began to understand just how important it was for her mother to find her happiness in her own way — and in her own home.

"They all spoke so highly and fondly of you, Mum," she said quietly, trying to control the quiver in her voice. "Made me feel quite proud."

She paused to take a deep breath before she was able to continue.

"You used to say how much I was like Dad. I just hope . . . I hope I grow to be more like you."

Marion's eyes were misted as they looked at her daughter.

"You can thank your dad for what I am now, dear," she said, and smiled at her daughter's puzzled expression.

"Do you remember how house-proud I used to be? Your dad often gave me a row for it. Used to say we can always get more paint, or buy a new chair, but we can't buy friends or loved ones, and they're what make a home really worth living in.

"It was only after he'd gone that I really understood that. I want to make up for it now, while I still have the time."

Anne couldn't speak, the emotion was swelling inside her so strongly. Then she laughed and brushed a tear from her cheek.

"What's so funny?" her mum asked, surprised.

"I was just thinking . . . that's the kind of thing Bill would say."

"I know, my dear. That's why I keep telling you how lucky you are."

"That's quite true." Anne nodded. "I am lucky, very lucky." □

Wishful Thinking

SOMETIMES, when I gaze at
      Mum,
   With baby on her knee,
I dream about the time she was
   A little girl like me.

A little girl whose name was Jill,
   A tomboy, so they say,
Who'd turn a cartwheel with the
      best,
   And sing the livelong day.

A girl with two long pony-tails,
   A cheeky, laughing face,
Whose school reports said:
      "Good at games,
   "But spelling's a disgrace."

Everybody likes my mum,
   She's sensible and kind,
A wee bit bossy, truth to tell,
   But I don't really mind.

For every now and then I glimpse
   A twinkle in her eye,
And I can see that little girl
   She was in days gone by.

A girl who loved to hop and
      skip,
   To clamber up a tree . . .
Oh, how I wish I'd known my
      mum
   When she was small, like me!

— *Kathleen O'Farrell.*

73

by
MARGRET
GERAGHTY

All For Gran!

I T all happened so quickly. One moment, Edna was scurrying past the carol singers outside the pizzeria. The next she was sprawling sideways on a patch of ice.

Her shopping flew from her grasp. Her arm thwacked the pavement and she saw tangerines rolling in all directions like a bag of snooker balls.

Oh, no! They'll all be bruised, was her first anguished thought. She put out an impatient hand and tried to rise.

But her arm felt as though someone were trying to run through it with an electric sewing machine. She winced and looked up at a cluster of white, silent faces.

Then suddenly, people were talking.

"She's hurt . . . fetch an ambulance . . . poor old thing."

Poor old thing? That's *me* they're talking about, Edna thought, bridling and making another attempt to struggle to her feet.

"No, no, don't move. You might have broken something."

A woman in a shiny mackintosh dropped to her knees and slipped something soft under her head.

Edna panicked, tried to move her foot, and was rewarded with such a vicious pain that she almost let fly with an undignified yelp. Then she heard the distant wail of an ambulance and everything went black.

Edna came out of hospital at the weekend.

"I feel like Tutankhamen." She giggled as, with her foot and arm bandaged, she allowed herself to be helped into her son's roomy car.

Max grinned. "Let's be thankful you didn't fall in one of those godforsaken lanes around your cottage. Or you might have been joining the Pharaohs sooner than you thought!"

He arranged a woollen rug across her knees.

"Now remember, Mother —" his brown eyes grew serious "— we've been given permission to take you home on one condition. No exertion! That means you're to allow yourself to be waited on for once in your life. D'you understand?"

Edna nodded obediently. And then for no reason at all she tried to remember how old Max had been when he'd learned to cross the road without holding her hand.

Now look at him — strong and capable, with a company car and two children, and a wife who never made steamed puddings because of something called "cholesterol."

"Everything's arranged," Max continued smoothly, switching on the engine. "I've locked up your cottage and cancelled the milk so you've got nothing to worry about. Just sit back and look forward to a family Christmas."

"But are you sure it isn't going to be too much extra work?" she murmured anxiously. "For Ruth, I mean."

Max turned and patted her knee. "I've told you already. Don't worry! If there's one thing Ruth's good at, it's organisation. You should know that."

Edna did. Her daughter-in-law was one of that new breed of superwomen who never had an empty tea caddy or migraine headaches. Ruth planned. Everything. Right down to the fillings on next week's sandwiches.

I'm so lucky, Edna told herself, thinking of all the elderly people who had to manage with an ancient gas fire and Meals-on-Wheels.

"Here we are," Max said, pulling to a halt outside his house. He carried her up the steps into the pastel-painted hall.

WELCOME home, Mother!" Ruth stepped warmly forward, touching each of Edna's cheeks with the scented softness of her own. "Tea's ready."

Edna smiled happily, only resisting when Max tried to carry her down the passage to the sitting-room.

"I have to have a little exercise," she remonstrated gently, reaching for her crutches. "Or my joints will lock."

Max looked doubtful. "Well, don't overdo it, not just yet. It'll be weeks before you're fully fit."

For some strange reason his words bothered her, filled her with a vague sense of unease. How silly! She put them out of her mind, and later that night as she lay warm and snug in the spare bedroom, she realised afresh how thankful she was to be out of hospital.

The nurses had been wonderful, of course, but even their cheery banter couldn't compensate for the continual swishing of curtains and clattering of bedpans — not to mention the gluey smell of canteen gravy.

And it would be such bliss not to be woken by the sound of coughing at one o'clock in the morning.

She snuggled down between the smooth sheets and fell asleep.

★　　　★　　　★　　　★

With Max and Ruth, Edna's days began to fall into a pattern.

Every morning before leaving for work, Max carried her downstairs and arranged her on the sofa with her bad foot on a padded stool.

Ruth had given her a small brass bell, which she had only to ring once for someone to come running.

"Cup of tea, Granny," young Adam would say, stepping carefully into the room with a tray of Lapsang — Ruth never bought Indian because of the tannin.

Behind Adam was Sophie, one hand in her mouth, the other clutching a toy thermometer and half a stethoscope.

"Cake, Granny?" Adam continued, proffering a plate of chocolate swiss roll.

"Not you!" He swept his sister's eager fingers smartly aside. "It's too near Christmas and cake's bad for your teeth."

Sophie's lip jutted. "What about Granny's teeth, then?"

"Don't be ridiculous." His eyes rolled with eight-year-old scorn. "Grannies don't have real teeth."

"Don't believe you, don't believe you!" Sophie chanted, her head nevertheless tilting as she tried to see into Edna's mouth.

"It's true. They have to buy them at the dentist and keep them in a jar, like goldfish. Isn't that right, Granny?"

Edna opened her mouth to explain gently that not only were her teeth all her own but she hadn't had to pay a penny for them, when Ruth, alerted by Sophie's chanting, hurried into the room and called the children away.

"You mustn't tire Granny." Edna heard her whispering as she ushered them into the kitchen. "Leave her to drink her tea in peace."

Edna felt suddenly rather old.

IT was on Tuesday that Max dropped his bombshell. The children had gone to bed. Ruth was in the kitchen, batchbaking mince pies.

The sitting-room was quiet, warmly intimate in the soft glow from the fairy lights which glimmered like precious jewels on the Christmas tree.

"Sherry, Mother?" Max asked.

"No thank you, dear," Edna said. "That was a delicious dinner. I always think you can't beat lamb for flavour."

"Mm." He was distracted, stroking a hesitant finger around the rim of his glass. And then in he dived.

"We were wondering — that is, Ruth and I were wondering — how you'd feel about coming to live with us permanently?"

Edna felt her heart beating against her chest. Her sense of unease returned, growing stronger.

"We could arrange everything for you," Max continued. "Sell the cottage, transport any little personal items you wanted to keep. We've got plenty of room and I can always build extra cupboards in the spare bedroom."

Edna suddenly found herself at a loss for words. So she said nothing, which was probably terribly rude, but she couldn't help it.

"Anyway," Max continued, "you think about it, Mother, and let us know. All right?"

She was so lucky, Edna insisted to herself as she struggled to grasp the full implications of the generous offer.

Most senior ladies would be overjoyed at such a gesture. Growing old and frail was no disgrace. It happened to everyone, eventually . . . It was just that she hadn't anticipated it happening quite so soon.

Then there was her cottage. Edna rocked fretfully on her sofa. More than anything, the thought of leaving her cottage, with its chintz curtains and its floorboards that seemed to creak in sympathy with her own bones, was a prospect almost too bleak to contemplate.

But contemplate it she must, and the following day she was so absorbed in her meditations that she didn't even notice her grandson watching her from the doorway.

"Why are you always looking out of the window, Granny?" he said suddenly. "Don't you like it here?"

Edna felt her heart turn over.

"Of course I do, silly." She pulled him to her, rumpling his silky hair.

"Our budgie used to look out the window all the time," Adam said carefully. "And then one day Sophie left his cage open and he flew away." His eyes were troubled.

Edna hugged him. "Well, I'm not a budgie, darling, and I'm not going to disappear without telling anyone — " she hesitated " — but I do have a little cottage, you know, and cottages sometimes get lonely on their own."

SHOULD she have said that, she wondered later. He might tell Max or Ruth. How ungrateful it would sound to them. She sighed and wished she had some knitting to keep herself occupied. But with a gammy arm, what could she do?

Across the hall, she could hear the throb of the washing machine. Oh, the thought of being free to iron all those clean clothes, listening to the hiss of steam on collars and cuffs, turning damp cotton into knife-edged tea-towels. What bliss!

She flicked determinedly through the television magazines — a daytime soap opera in California, followed by a keep-fit programme and yet another discussion on the pros and cons of soft margarine. Somehow she couldn't face any of them.

I'm turning into a cantankerous old woman, she thought crossly and her eyes turned inevitably towards the window. Not that there was much to see. A small paved square with a Japanese cherry tree in the centre.

In the spring it shed its blossoms rather prettily over the pavement, like pink marshmallow. In the winter it was as dead as old fusewire.

The back garden was much the same. Concrete paving slabs in a pattern of red and yellow that reminded Edna of shop-bought

Battenburg, a few terracotta pots of trailing ivy and a black plastic dustbin. Max and Ruth didn't have much interest in gardening.

Edna thought of her own small cottage and its stock of winter flowering bulbs, slender green spears of life pushing their way through the frozen earth. Then her thoughts drifted to the coton-easters, laden with berries like bunches of aniseed balls, the crimson flowering heathers, the prickly ilex outside the west window of her sitting-room . . .

Sternly she told herself that people were more important than plants and buildings. To mourn a cottage and its garden that she might never see again was an act of pure sentimentality. But however hard she tried, she couldn't quite make this idea stick.

Christmas was coming. Tomorrow would be Christmas Eve. Adam and Sophie were making streamers to decorate the hall. Ruth was sitting down for once, revising a last-minute shopping list.

▶ *over*

PARTNERQUOTES

SOPHIA LOREN

"Everything I have in life I owe to Carlo."
"In Naples we have a proverb: 'Love is made of little things.' "
On being jailed for 16 days for tax evasion: *"It is an experience which has enriched my soul."*
"I don't really admire people for their looks — but for their personalities . . ."

CARLO PONTI

"I saw in Sophia all the best that is Italian — not just Neapolitan gaiety, but a vitality, sensitivity and a sense of rhythm that no Actor's Studio can teach.
She was not an actress, she was an artiste."

SOPHIA LOREN & CARLO PONTI — AGAINST ALL ODDS

Max was . . . yes, where was Max? It sounded as though he were sawing up logs, but as the house had no open fire, he couldn't be.

"He's, uh, putting up a shelf in the hall," Ruth said in answer to her query.

Edna saw Ruth's eyes drop hurriedly to her paper, and was seized with a sudden terrible notion that Max was building something for the spare bedroom.

She thought she had persuaded him to wait until after Christmas for her decision. It seemed he had pre-empted her, on the assumption that her answer was going to be yes.

"Well, it's making my head ache." The words were out before she could stop them. She slumped back on the sofa, not daring to look at Ruth. She could just imagine the hurt in her eyes.

"I'm sorry," she mumbled. "That was very rude."

"Don't worry about it, Mother." Ruth's voice was soothing. "I'll tell him to stop."

"I'll be fine in a while." She managed a tremulous smile.

Ruth patted her on the shoulder. "It's all right."

If only it were, thought Edna bleakly.

CHRISTMAS DAY at last — not snow, but a thick hoar frost that cloaked and muted the colours of the outside world. Edna put her heartsearching to one side, pretending it could be popped into a polythene bag and sealed until the day was over.

Just live for the moment, she told herself. Tomorrow will come soon enough.

At eleven o'clock, Ruth brought in the mince pies and a jug of coffee.

Max smiled indulgently as the children leapt to their feet.

"Time to open the presents. Granny first!" Adam shouted, while Sophie rolled on the floor.

"Good idea. Come on, Adam." Max turned to Edna. "We just have to pop next door. Won't be long."

Oh, no, Edna thought, feeling faint. He's gone to fetch his woodwork. It must be at least a new cupboard if it's too big to hide inside the house.

She looked nervously at Ruth, who was smiling as she poured the coffee.

Three minutes later, father and son returned. Max was cradling something in his arms — something that squeaked and wriggled.

Edna gasped as an animal's face appeared from under Max's elbow. Next moment the creature was on the floor, scurrying across the carpet, a plump, blonde viking of a puppy, with a beige and black nose like a two-tone rubber.

"Oh!" Edna cried. "He's absolutely adorable, but why . . . ?" Her voice faded as Max put his arm around her shoulders.

"It's OK, Mother. We can read the signs. We know you want to go home when you're better."

"Oh dear." Edna felt her cheeks burning, but a great burden rolled from her heart as though she were discarding a painful shoe. "You must think me so ungrateful."

"We think no such thing." Ruth's voice was gentle as she tried to disengage the hem of her skirt from the puppy's mouth. "We jumped the gun, that's all. We want you to be happy."

"And we're going to train this little fellow specially so he doesn't pull you over in the lanes," Max said. "We'll feel a lot happier knowing he's there watching over you."

"This is the best Christmas present I've ever had." Edna felt her voice breaking as tears sprang to her eyes.

A Real Christmas

A MERRY Christmas everyone,
　You'll hear the people say.
But, tell me, where has Christmas gone,
　Have we forgotten how to play?

Time was when Santa Claus would call,
　And all of us believed.
He'd bring us toys, a bat and ball,
　A magic spell was weaved.

Party time with friends all round,
　To join in all the fun.
Sweet memories of this are found,
　By you and everyone.

So tell me where has Christmas gone,
　With love to fill the heart.
When glittering little candles shone,
　And chestnuts in the hearth.

Let's turn to Christ at Christmas time,
　To him, let us speak.
He will help us all to find,
　The happiness we seek.

Oh Lord, I am a poor man,
　Gifts I cannot buy.
Provide for me the lost lamb,
　Lord, do you hear my cry?

Christmas is a time for love,
　That everyone can share.
A gift that's from the Lord above,
　Reject it — who would dare?

My wish for you at Christmas time,
　Is happiness, health and cheer.
A smile that from the eyes will shine,
　And last throughout the year.

— *H. F. Molesworth.*

"There's more!" Sophie could hardly contain her excitement. "S'under the tree."

Max looked embarrassed. "It's really nothing. Just something I knocked together. Thought it might help pass the time while the weather's bad. Here." He thust an angular package on to her lap.

Edna removed the string and paper to reveal — a wooden birdtable.

"That's the spare shelf in the hall," Ruth said, laughing.

"Daddy's going to fix it outside the sitting-room so you won't be bored no more," Adam added.

Edna held out her good arm and drew them to her, Max, Ruth, Adam and Sophie, while the puppy leapt on to the sofa.

"I'm so lucky," she whispered. And this time she really meant it. □

STRANGER IN A STRANGE LAND

E VERYTHING all right, madam?" Beth stifled the sob that was rising in her throat and summoned a half-smile for the air-hostess. "Yes, just fine, thanks."

Oh, stop being such a baby, she mentally scolded herself. You've been on this plane for nearly seven hours now, and you *still* haven't stopped crying! Grow up!

But the more she thought about why she was crying, the more upset she became.

They'd all come to Atlanta Airport to see her off, the whole family — even Great-Granny Davies and she was all of ninety-one! And she wouldn't see them again for . . . Oh, she didn't know how long!

Of course, she hadn't let them see how awful she felt. Not for the world would she have upset her mother by bursting into tears. *That* wasn't the memory to leave them with. And after all, she should be feeling happy . . . And she *was* . . .

You're going to Scotland to be with Bob, she reminded herself, and the thought cheered her. She had so much to tell him. Two months is a long time to be apart when you're newlyweds.

Beth twisted the slim gold ring on her finger. Only five months married and they'd been apart for two of them. She'd always known that marriage to a Navy man would mean moves and separations.

by ANN MacCOLL

82

No-one could say she hadn't been warned. It was all part of the life she'd taken on when she'd become Bob's wife, and they'd agreed that was how it should be.

But somehow it had been much easier in theory, and the thought of travelling abroad had seemed more exciting then than it did right now! And anyway, they hadn't expected a move so soon!

And what a move! To Drumbrae, in the North of Scotland! They'd looked it up on the map together and couldn't believe how far north it was. Why, it was almost on the same latitude as Alaska, and as far north as Moscow! Boy, would it be cold! And for folk from as far south in the United States as them, it would take some getting used to!

"Don't forget to pack your snow shoes," and "Say 'hi' to the Eskimos for us!" Their friends had thought it was a great joke!

"You'll have to build an igloo, Beth," her father had teased, and at the thought of her kind, caring dad, the tears started to rise again.

Ashamed, she turned her face to the window . . . Land! She could see land! She looked up and a passing stewardess caught the question in her eyes.

"Yes, we're almost there." And as she spoke, the jet began its slow descent.

YOU'LL love it here, Beth," Bob said for the umpteenth time as they drove up the A9. "The house is pretty ordinary, but you'll soon make it into a home. But what a view we've got. You'll love it."

Beth smiled at him reassuringly. "Don't worry. I'll be fine. I'm feeling much happier now I'm with you. It doesn't seem so terrifying.

"Although," she couldn't help adding, a twinkle in her eye, "I still think you're driving on the wrong side of the road!"

"Oh, you'll soon get used to that." Bob grinned. "Look, Pitlochry's just up ahead. It's supposed to be really nice. What do you say we stop there for something to eat?"

It was late when they reached Drumbrae, and Beth was exhausted. She seemed to have been travelling for ever. The journey north had been slow — it was late November and they'd been in darkness for most of the way, and Bob, unaccustomed to the winding, sometimes tricky roads, wasn't keen to hurry.

Beth, buoyed up with the excitement of being with her husband once again, was happy at first. But eventually she found herself wishing the journey was over.

And now, driving through the dimly-lit, empty village street, she felt awful, and when Bob led her into the house which would be their home for the next three years, she was near to tears.

As she stared round the small, bare living-room, the look on her face gave her feelings away. Bob took her in his arms.

"Don't worry, Beth. We'll soon make it look good. We were lucky to get it so soon. A lot of couples have to go into digs at first. This is our home now."

At that, all Beth's resilience suddenly, unashamedly crumbled. "Oh, Bob, I'm so homesick! I want to go home! Why did we have to leave the States? I'll never settle here. It's all so different!"

"Oh, Beth, please don't cry, not now we're together again. It won't be easy at first, but I just know you'll get to like it. You've never really been away from home before, and you must be exhausted with all this travelling. Things'll seem better in the morning, you'll see."

Will they? Beth wondered. I doubt it.

IN spite of being so desperately tired — or perhaps because of it — Beth couldn't sleep. The strange bed, the strange room, the newness of having Bob at her side once again, all these things unsettled her. She tossed and turned, and watched the sky slowly lighten.

And she puzzled over the strange noise in the background that she just couldn't place.

Was it the central heating? The refrigerator? She couldn't rightly say . . .

But at last, when Bob was rising to start his day shift, she fell into a deep and peaceful sleep.

When she finally awoke and looked at the clock by the bed, it was mid-afternoon. The house was quiet and only the wind and the occasional noise from the street below disturbed the peace — that and the same strange, rhythmically soothing sound she had heard the night before.

She lay for ages, slowly waking, collecting her thoughts.

But what was that sound?

"It's the sea!" she exclaimed aloud. "It must be!"

She leapt up and ran to the window. Apart from on the plane — and the television, of course, she'd never seen the sea! Never even been close to it.

A young woman from America's mid-west didn't see the sea unless she travelled, and until now, Beth never had.

It was almost a standing joke between Bob and her. Imagine being married to a Navy man and never having seen the sea! Mind you, Bob, despite his career, hadn't seen that much of it either. His expertise lay in communications and most of his postings had been to inland Naval stations.

It was at a social function at his base that they'd first met.

She gazed from the bedroom window, spellbound by the view. Just a few hundred yards away lay the most beautiful sandy bay. She'd known they'd be living near the sea — but not that they'd be right bang up beside it! Bob must have meant this to be a surprise!

It was a wild, windy day and Beth watched in awe as the waves crashed in upon the shore. It was incredible!

The sun played on the water, making it glisten and shine. The hills beyond were bathed in dancing sunlight — but the sky behind them . . .

It was so startingly black that Beth caught her breath. What a contrast! Sunlight and shadows combined to add drama to the scene that she would scarcely have believed possible.

Beth gazed out at the beach until she began to shiver from the cold. Then she dressed in her warmest clothes and hurried downstairs to look round.

The house was sparsely furnished with only the bare essentials. What there was, was old fashioned and clumsy, not at all in keeping with a modern house. The living-room had few redeeming features, except that it was clean and neat, the walls were freshly painted and the carpet was obviously new.

She walked through to the kitchen and automatically reached for the kettle. A coffee and something to eat would make her feel better.

The kitchen was small and plain, but it did have one thing in its favour — the large window looked out on to the beach, with the same view over the road to the bay beyond as she'd seen from the bedroom.

Beth went to the refrigerator and reached for the milk. There was none. She peered inside. There was practically nothing there! Obviously Bob didn't realise they had to eat to live!

She took her jacket from the corner where she'd thrown it the night before, checked her purse and decided she might as well try out the local shops.

A BRISK walk took her down the near-empty street to the centre of the village, where a small shop stood sandwiched between a hotel and the post office.

Feeling slightly nervous — this was, after all, her first solo venture out in a foreign country — Beth pushed open the shop door and stepped in.

She was pleasantly surprised to find that the place resembled a small supermarket, and she wandered round at leisure, carefully selecting what she thought they would need to last them till the weekend. On Saturday they could take a trip to the nearest town and buy their groceries there.

Placing her basket on the counter by the door, she waited patiently for someone to come and serve her. But the shop was deserted.

After a few minutes she gave a hesitant cough, and when this produced no result she began to feel annoyed.

At last, after knocking several times, a sour-looking woman came through from the back shop and almost snatched the basket from her. Without a word of apology for the delay, she rang up the total on the till and waited, stony faced until Beth fumbled with the unfamiliar currency to produce the right amount.

All the pleasant words of chat she'd planned as she'd collected her provisions just wouldn't come.

The shopkeeper took her money without a word, and watched her silently as she made for the door. Beth couldn't get out fast enough!

Thoroughly miserable, she raced homewards, mortified to feel tears

 ▶ *p88*

A Gipsy's Dream

MY life of freedom, over now, will
never be beyond recall,
I'm now confined within four walls with
roof and chimneys tall;
Sometimes at night my thoughts stray
far beyond restricting door,
I feel the wind upon my face, the
sweep of open moor.

I walk the lanes of springtime green
and smell the hawthorn sweet,
I tread so light to feel springy grass
beneath my feet,
I see the starry sky of night and smell
the woodsmoke fire,
Then I awake and my whole being
aches with wild desire,
I live on dreams and past delights and
bow to fate's decree,
Knowing that no-one could steal a
single memory.

— *Georgina Hall.*

prick her eyes again. In all the time since she'd left home, she'd hardly stopped crying!

Letting herself in at the front door, she dropped the food on a living-room chair. One quick look round the empty room made her realise she couldn't stay there a moment longer.

Without thinking, Beth hurried outside and raced across the road on to the beach. Then she ran and ran, hair flying in the breeze, tears stinging her cheeks, head throbbing, until at last she could run no further.

She flung herself down on the sand, not caring that it was cold and damp, and sobbed her heart out. She should never have come — she hated it here — she wasn't welcome . . . She'd never felt so alone and miserable in her entire life!

Nobody can cry for ever, and at last, exhausted, Beth's sobs began to subside. But still she lay stretched out on the cold, wet sand, too miserable to notice the dampness seeping through her clothes.

Then suddenly, through her misery, she became aware that she wasn't alone.

Without lifting her head, Beth glanced out of the corner of her eye and saw a pair of sodden, sand-covered trainers. She looked up past the bare legs, scruffy shorts and anorak, and into large, innocent brown eyes, framed by a thatch of sand-coloured, tousled hair.

WHY are you crying?" the boy asked bluntly, and Beth was immediately struck by the soft, lilting tones of his accent.

She sat up at once, and smoothed down her hair.

"Are you OK?"

Beth shook her head. "Not really," she admitted frankly. "I feel terrible. My head's sore and my throat hurts."

"That's because you've been crying!" the child went on. "You look awful."

"Thanks."

He was honest, at least, Beth thought ruefully.

"You'll catch your death lying on the sand on a day like this, you know. It's not the middle of summer!"

"I know that!"

"You're an American, aren't you?"

Beth nodded.

"Is that why you're crying?"

Beth almost smiled. "Because I'm an American?"

"No, silly! Because you're not in America now!"

"Yes, that's why I'm crying." She sighed deeply. There was no point in pretending.

The boy sat down beside her.

"This is the best place in the whole world," he said seriously.

"Have you ever been anywhere else?"

"No."

"Then how do you know it's the best?"

"My grandfather says it is."

"And has *he* ever been anywhere else?" Beth asked, a touch sarcastically.

"Of course he has! He's been everywhere! He was a sailor and he's been all round the world, and he says there's nowhere as bonnie and friendly as Drumbrae."

"I suppose he ought to know," Beth said. But I doubt it, she thought miserably.

"Och, you'll soon love it here." There wasn't a hint of doubt in the boy's voice. "What's your name?" he asked suddenly.

"Elizabeth Mills. But call me Beth. All my friends do." She smiled and immediately felt much better.

"I'm Alexander Donald Neil MacDonald," the boy said proudly. "But everyone just calls me Sandy — it's short for Alexander, you know, and they say I've got sandy hair."

"You sure have!" Beth found herself laughing. "It's full of the stuff!"

Sandy grinned. "You've got a nice smile," he said.

"Thanks! You're not so bad yourself!" She brushed the sand from her jeans. "We'd better get up from here, Sandy," she said, beginning to feel uncomfortable. "Do you mind if I walk with you for a while?"

"Of course not. You can help me gather shells, if you like. My gran uses them to decorate trinket boxes for selling to the tourists in the summer," he explained.

"All right," Beth agreed. "And you can tell me everything you know about them. My youngest brother, Jason, is about your age. He'd be really interested. I'll maybe send him some."

THEY started towards the far end of the beach, not saying much, just walking in companionable silence. From time to time Sandy showed her something he'd found, or pointed out places of interest in the distance.

Beth was feeling more relaxed than she'd been in days. The young boy's presence was soothing, and she was impressed by how much he knew about the sea and the wildlife around him.

The wind had dropped considerably, and she felt warmer now, although she was still uncomfortable in her damp clothes. But she was reluctant to go home to her empty house. Here was an escape, even if it was only temporary.

Slowly she became aware of someone shouting in the distance. Sandy heard it, too, and looked up towards a cottage on the hillside, which Beth noticed for the first time.

"That's my gran calling," Sandy said. "Come on up and meet her," he invited and immediately dashed off, leaving Beth no choice but to follow.

At once her heart began to race. She couldn't face another rejection. But already Sandy had reached the cottage and was talking to his grandmother. It wouldn't be fair to refuse his invitation either . . .

Beth left the beach and began the climb up to the house. Minutes later she was met by a smiling, elderly woman.

"Hello, I'm Effie, Sandy's gran. It's nice to meet you."

Beth shook the hand that was held out in welcome. "Beth Mills. Pleased to meet you."

"Sandy tells me you're an American lady just come to live in Drumbrae. Well, well, that's just grand," the old lady said. "Now come on in and take a seat by the fireside. You must be frozen on a day like this."

At once her sharp eyes noticed Beth's damp clothes. "What did you do, lass?" she asked. "You're soaking!"

"She fell on the wet sand, Gran," Sandy said at once, and Beth shot him a grateful look.

"You're not hurt, I hope?"

Beth shook her head. "No, I'm fine, thanks."

"Oh, that's good. Well, come in and get dried out."

She led her into the cottage, and Beth caught her breath. It was like stepping back in time! She'd never seen anything like it!

The room was small, the furniture old and there was a beautiful, black-leaded fireplace on one wall. Everything shone brightly with polish.

Sitting next to the fire was a rugged-faced old man, puffing quietly on a pipe. He looked as if he hadn't a care in the world!

Sandy led her over to meet him. "This is my grandad," he said. "Grandad, this is Beth, my new friend."

The old man put out his hand. "Pleased to meet you, Beth. It's Dougie they call me. Sit down and warm yourself while Effie gets a wee bite of something for you to eat."

B ETH sat down gratefully and let the warmth of the fire engulf her. She felt at peace with herself as she listened to Sandy's easy chatter, and watched Effie busy herself round the kitchen table. The "wee bite of something" turned out to be plates loaded with delicious home baking.

"What's that lovely smell?" Beth sniffed the air. "I've never come across a fire like that before."

"That's peat, lass," Dougie explained, and Beth listened enthralled as he described the work that was done to keep the family warm through the winter months.

"Of course, a lot of people use machines for cutting the peat

▶ *over*

═PARTNERQUOTES═

JOHN BARRYMORE

1930s: *"She walked into the studio like a charming child — slender and shy and golden haired. I never saw such radiance. My God! I knew she was the one I had been waiting for all my life . . ."*

On receiving help from a friend when he was in financial trouble through his passion for alcohol: *"I shall burn a candle for you, in some great cathedral. I shall, of course, burn it at both ends."*

DOLORES COSTELLO

was 24 years younger than John Barrymore and the daughter of Maurice Costello — the first idol of the screen. She remained always a private person. They were married for seven years and had two children.

JOHN BARRYMORE & DOLORES COSTELLO — A SUDDEN LOVE

nowadays," Dougie finished sadly. "But there's nothing to beat the old-fashioned way if you want a job well done."

Effie laughed. "Oh, you silly old fool. If you were offered a peat cutter you'd jump at the chance of it. You know fine you would."

Dougie's look spoke volumes, but "Ach, away with you, woman!" was all he said.

Beth smiled, warming to the old couple more and more.

"And do you like living in Drumbrae?" Effie asked.

"I only arrived last night," Beth explained. "So I don't really know yet."

"You'll be feeling a wee bit homesick, then?"

Beth nodded, the familiar lump coming into her throat.

"Och, yes, it's a terrible thing the homesickness," Effie went on. "I mind it fine."

"Oh, really?" Beth prompted, interested.

"Two nights in the hospital at Inverness were enough for me," she said vehemently. "I missed Drumbrae and the sea so bad that I swore I'd never leave here again. And I never have. It's been home all my born days."

Beth smiled warmly at her. "I've lived in the same place all my life, too," she said. "So this is quite a change for me."

"You'll like being near the sea, of course," Dougie put in. "Everybody does."

"Well, until today I'd never seen the sea before . . ."

Sandy and Effie gasped.

"Never seen the sea?" Effie was shocked.

Dougie shook his head in disbelief. "Well, well," he muttered. "Well, well, well . . ." And took another draw on his pipe.

"Take another scone, Beth," Effie urged. "You need fattening up."

Beth laughed and did as she was told.

"So you won't have met anyone in Drumbrae yet?" the old woman went on.

"Well," Beth hesitated, "I did meet the woman in the shop this morning — but I'm afraid she wasn't very friendly."

Effie shook her head. "Oh, that would be poor Miss MacKenzie. It's such a shame . . . The poor cratur lost her brother just last week. She's looked after him for years and she's taking it very bad, you know. But she won't even close the shop for a few days to have a break.

"She thinks it's best to keep herself occupied, but I don't think it's doing the soul much good . . ."

"Oh dear, I'm sorry about that," Beth said, meaning it. "I didn't stop to think there might be a reason for her behaviour — I just thought that maybe strangers weren't very welcome here, I'm afraid."

Effie looked at her kindly. "You mustn't think that, lass. Everyone's welcome in Drumbrae, if they're decent folk. It's the friendliest place in the world to those who want to belong."

Beth smiled. "Yes, since meeting you all I'm beginning to believe that."

Suddenly she noticed the clock on the mantelpiece and jumped up. "I'm so sorry, I really must run. I didn't realise what time it was — Bob'll be home shortly and if I'm not there he'll be worried."

"I understand." Effie nodded.

"He's worried about how I'll settle in," Beth explained.

Dougie shot her a wide, toothless smile. "Now don't be a stranger," he said. "You know where we are, and we'll want to see more of you!"

"You can bet on it." Beth grinned as she headed for the door.

"Wait a minute!" Sandy jumped up. "I'm coming with you."

"Isn't it getting a bit dark for you to be going out? I'll manage alone," Beth assured him.

"But I live in the village!" he informed her. "You'll have to come over and see my mum tomorrow. She'd love to meet you. Come on." He grabbed her hand and pulled her outside. "It's still light enough to find a few more shells for Jason on the way home."

Beth laughed and looked back at the old woman standing in the doorway.

"Thanks for everything, Effie," she called.

"Now remember, don't be a stranger!"

"Oh, I won't!" Beth shouted back. "You can count on it!"

A S she and Sandy made their way homewards, Beth took the time to look around her. In the distance the sun was setting low in red-golden sky. And in the East the moon was already rising, and it comforted her to think that this was the same moon that her family would look up and see hours from now.

She wasn't really so far from home. They were all under the same sky, and people were kind wherever you went. It was her own fault for being too tied up in her own problems to think that others had their troubles, too. She'd treat the sad and lonely lady in the shop with a lot more understanding in future.

She watched Sandy splash through the pools of water on the sand and thought of her youngest brother, so like him. Maybe Sandy's family would be her Scottish family in time. If they were all as nice as he was, she was sure she'd love them!

Beth stopped and took a deep breath. What a wonderful smell! She hadn't noticed the sharp, salt tang of the sea before . . . There was so much to learn. Tomorrow she would explore and really get to know her new home.

"Come on, slowcoach!" Sandy called. "We'd better be home before dark. Look, there's my mother out at the roadside crying on me! Typical! She's always worrying, that one. Come on and meet her!"

Beth laughed and quickened her pace, her homesickness fading as she walked.

Oh, she had so much to tell Bob! □

B UT why do you suddenly want to go to Glasgow?" Sarah looked baffled — and not for the first time since her Great-Aunt Jenny had arrived from Australia. "It's such a long way from Binworth!"

It was incredible that this serene, white-haired woman sitting opposite her was, in fact, her great-aunt, her grandmother's sister. She was so amazingly youthful, and spritely.

For her part, Jenny Martin hadn't missed the shrill note in young Sarah's voice. Experience with her own children at that age told her that something was wrong — probably a quarrel with that handsome boyfriend of hers!

But in her wisdom, Jenny said nothing. She was very glad that Sarah was popping in so often to this small apartment she had rented for a few months. Glad, too, that Sarah's mother understood her wish to be independent, so that she could come and go without feeling she was disturbing anyone.

"It's really a very long story," Jenny said with a little smile. "It all goes back to the war years, when I was in the WRNS, and my first base was near Glasgow in 1943.

"Were you married then?"

"Oh, goodness me no. I hadn't even met your uncle John. I had only just turned nineteen." Jenny chuckled. "We met later when I was stationed at a submarine base. We were going to be married in the last year of the war. But then his submarine was sent on a mission the day before our wedding — and there was no time to do anything about it."

Sarah looked at her, horrified. "But how *awful*. How on earth did you bear it?"

"Oh, we learned to put up with catastrophe in those days. But mind you, it was a bit hard at the time!"

by
KATE
MORTIMER

GETTING TOGETHER

"I'd have died," Sarah said. "I don't know how you can be so cheerful about it."

Sarah regarded her great-aunt thoughtfully. She was beginning to understand, just a little, how her aunt had managed to cope when her husband died so suddenly a couple of years ago. How, and why, she'd had the courage to sell her home, and take a trip back to her birthplace.

"One of the people I want to see in Glasgow," Jenny Martin went on, musingly, "is a girl who at the time had a young baby, and her husband was in the RAF. The fear and tension for her were dreadful, and she was only a couple of years older than I."

"And was he . . . did he . . . come back safely?" Sarah asked.

"I don't know. At the end of the war your uncle John wrote to say he'd got a good job in Australia. Of course, I went out to him . . . and lost touch with Mary. But I've never forgotten her . . ." Jenny's voice tailed away.

"And by now her baby will be grown up and have children?"

"I suppose . . ."

Jenny was remembering the day she was turning out an old trunk, after selling off most of her home and its contents.

The box was full of her wartime memories and she had come across Mary's address in an old diary. She'd remembered the tram journey out to Milngavie . . .

It was odd, how in that moment she had seemed to see Mary as she had been, to hear her voice, her brave laughter while she was waiting for news.

"I'm going to Glasgow, to find Mary and see how life's treated her," she'd promised herself, feeling a strange uplifting of her spirit. It was as if her planned trip to Britain had gained a new purpose.

S ARAH'S voice broke into her thoughts.

"I . . . have you realised that she might not be there any more?" the girl was asking hesitantly. "She might not even be in Glasgow any more."

Jenny looked across at the pretty, golden-haired girl perched on the footstool at her feet.

"Of course. But surely someone in the street will know where she's gone? And . . . well, she didn't answer my letters."

"Aunt Jenny," Sarah put in quickly, "I don't think you realise . . . I mean, I don't think you ought to go wandering around in a big city like Glasgow . . ."

"Fiddlesticks. It's a wonderful place — so friendly. Do you know I used to go to Loch Lomond, and Dunoon and Rothesay on my day off. Have you ever been to Glasgow, Sarah?"

"No," Sarah said. "I haven't."

Jenny looked at her intently, the sad, taut expression she recognised so well.

"Then it's high time you did," she said brightly. "Look, you've got another week before you start your new job. Come with me, even if

only for the weekend — I'm going on Friday. Please do come."
Sarah's eyes brightened. "Oh, what a wonderful idea! I'd love to get away . . . to have time to . . ." Suddenly, she actually laughed. "I'll tell you why when we're on our way!"

And she did, on Friday morning as the train headed northwards . . .

"Then Ben actually told me I was spoiled and selfish and needed taking down a few pegs!" Sarah finished.

"And you told him?" Jenny said mildly.

"I said he was domineering, bossy and self-opinionated and conceited and I never wanted to see him again. Then he walked out."

"And do you want to see him again?"

"No . . . yes. Well . . ."

"And I bet he wants to see you, too."

"I don't know. He's very strong minded. But . . ." She touched Jenny's hand affectionately. "When we were talking about the war the other day . . . well, it made me think. How awful it must have been never knowing whether . . ." Her eyes filled with tears.

"Now then, after this weekend you might see the way to . . . to cope with it," Jenny said cheerfully. "One thing, a quarrel is very rarely as bad as it seems. We're going to have a good meal tonight then a good night's rest."

"Bless you," Sarah said. "And tomorrow we're off to find your Mary — we hope! Let's hope the sun shines."

And it did, brilliantly. Only, as Jenny said regretfully, the only trams left were all in the museum. Well, at least she'd go and look at them before she moved on.

She must get some postcards of them, too, to send to her own grandchildren back in Australia.

ALTHOUGH Jenny thought she'd quite forgotten the little house in Milngavie she'd visited all those years ago, she recognised it immediately. The small garden at the front was bright with summer flowers, and there were pretty plants in the front window.

There were tears in her eyes as she rang the bell. This place had been such an oasis for her for a little while, in the midst of service life.

And standing beside her, young Sarah was remembering other things — wondering whether Ben was thinking about her, or whether he'd already found someone else.

She had lain awake all night, in her room at the small hotel where she and her aunt were staying, wondering . . . and thinking about that nineteen-year-old girl, over forty years ago, leaving her own room and her home. And being pitchforked into this big city, and WRNS quarters sharing with twenty-two other girls. Twenty-two . . . !

But Sarah's reverie was interrupted as the door was opened by a tall, balding, grey-haired man with blue eyes. He looked at them curiously, and for a few moments Jenny couldn't find her tongue.

Then abruptly she said, "I've come to see whether Mary Lister still lives here, or . . ."

The man smiled, and it was a warm and friendly smile.

"No, she doesn't," he said. "Are you a friend of hers?"

"I was," Jenny said. "It was during the war. I . . . actually, we met on a tram and she —"

At that the man laughed outright.

"Oh, now I know who you are. You were looking for a tram to a place called Mullguy — but spelt Milngavie. I'm Malcolm Craigie — Mary's brother."

He opened the door wide. "Come in and have a cup of tea."

The pretty living-room had different furniture, but was just as homely as Jenny remembered. She introduced Sarah, who sat entranced in a small rocking chair, listening to everything, as Malcolm told her aunt that Mary was now living in Aberdeen.

Yes, he said, Mary's husband had returned, but very ill, shattered by the war. But he and Mary had been thankful to have each other during the years they had together before the end came.

"I came to live here to help her with the nursing and lifting," Malcolm said. He smiled, wryly. "It took my mind off my own problems — I'd come back to find my girl had . . . well, she married an American soldier. Mary and I had been great buddies, and I loved her little boy, too."

Portrait Of The Heart Of Herts.!

THROUGH tree-lined walks and spreading fields,
And grassy banks that climb the new road,
By winding towpath of canal
While barges ply their heavy load.
By castle grounds and gracious walls
A little world of precious calm —
A place of history unique.
Of mellowed seasons' lasting charm.
Through lanes that lead by leafy woods.
Where dappled sunshine smoothly spills,
By scattered farms that nestle close
Among the sure, protecting hills.
By bridlepaths, through common's way,
Familiar routes at leisured pace,
To beckon as a quiet retreat,
And soothe the mind from life's mad race!
By copse and heath and sturdy oaks,
All set within a portrait fair —
To make the heart of Herts. for us
A place of pride for all to share!
— *Elizabeth Gozney.*

It seemed that now the little boy was a grown man, married with children of his own and living in Aberdeen. Mary had eventually remarried happily and was living near her son, and it was evident that Malcolm felt only pleasure in her contentment.

"Now I've retired she suggested I go up there, too. But . . . well, you know the song about belonging to Glasgow!" He laughed.

"Yes," Jenny told him. "I grew very fond of it, though when I first met Mary I was . . . unsettled."

"I know. When we first went into the forces, the lack of privacy was grim, wasn't it? Never a quiet place to be alone, to think."

"The marvellous thing was that Mary understood. After we'd started to talk that day on the tram, she told me I could come here any time and use her spare room to relax, write letters or whatever. It was *wonderful!*"

Jenny's eyes shone at the memory of Mary's kindness and imagination. "A pity I was drafted so soon afterwards!"

L IKE Malcolm, she had forgotten about Sarah, who was sitting just behind them, drinking in every word, fascinated, as Jenny filled in some of *her* story since the war.

"My children were marvellous when my husband died," Jenny told him, "and wanted me to share their homes. But I like to be independent and besides, I felt the need to do something positive — such as coming back to my roots for a while! To look up old friends, like Mary . . ."

"She'll want you to go and see her." Malcolm picked up a pad off the sideboard and wrote down the address. Then he noticed Sarah, sitting so silent.

"My dear girl," he said, "you must be bored stiff with all our reminiscing."

"Oh, no, I am not," Sarah said quickly. "You are making me think how lucky we are nowadays, whatever folk say. I mean . . ." her voice faltered ". . . if people my age today quarrel or . . . or anything, we don't have the fear that we might never be able to unsay awful things we have said. We don't have to wonder whether we . . . might not see each other ever again . . ."

Malcolm looked at her with an understanding smile.

"Ah, but there were many good things about it," he told her. "The comradeship, the feeling that we were all in it together doing a job that had to be done. And there was lots of laughter, too — wasn't there, Jenny?"

"Sure. And interest, and learning not to fuss."

"You know," Sarah said thoughtfully, "Dad's always said how resilient you were, Aunt Jenny. That you could turn your hand to anything and were tremendous fun to do things with. Now I know what he meant."

"Bless you," Jenny said gently. "Well, after you've listened to all our memories, I promise you we will have fun, exploring Glasgow. And tomorrow we'll go to Loch Lomond . . ."

She stood up then, and thanked Malcolm Craigie for his hospitality.

He looked hesitantly from one to the other, as if there was something else on his mind. But then Sarah said suddenly, "Could we go back to the hotel first, Auntie?" Her voice trembled a little. "Of course, Ben will probably be out but . . . but I'd like to phone him and see if he's at home."

"Of course. We'll go back right away . . ."

"Look," Malcolm said, "my car's outside. I'll give you a lift —

save your time waiting for buses. I won't take no for an answer!"

It took only ten minutes, and on the way Jenny chatted to ease the tension Sarah was evidently feeling now.

She told her how she'd gone to Luss for her first forty-eight-hour leave.

"We'll go there tomorrow," she promised. "You'll love it."

Outside the hotel, Malcolm Craigie seemed to understand that Sarah was aching to get to the telephone, so he just said a cheery goodbye, and hoped they'd enjoy their day in Glasgow.

For an instant, watching him drive away, Jenny thought how he must miss Mary, although he'd said he was so glad for her newly-found happiness.

He put his hand out of the car window and waved before turning the corner.

N OW," Jenny said briskly, "it will be easier for you to use the telephone in my room to ring Ben — no need to use this one in the hall. I'll wait until . . ."

"No, please come up with me," Sarah said tremulously.

So Jenny did just that, praying that Ben would be at home and not out with someone else.

It was soon evident that he was, and Sarah was pouring out everything about the journey to Scotland, and the visit they'd made that morning.

"Oh, Ben, it's made me feel so sorry . . . so guilty . . . what did you say?"

She suddenly began to laugh hysterically. "Oh, of course you weren't. Well, we were both silly idiots, that's what, and . . ."

There was another long pause. "Oh, Ben, would you, that would be wonderful. Oh, Aunt Jenny will be thrilled. Yes, yes . . ."

Eventually, the call ended and Sarah turned to her aunt with shining eyes.

"What do you think? He's coming up on the next train — do you think they'll have another room?"

"Yes," Jenny reassured her. "The receptionist told me they were never full at this time. Oh, that's marvellous. And now do your hair and tidy up and we're off to see . . . well, I think we'll go first to Kelvingrove."

The rest of the day passed on wings, and Sarah enjoyed seeing the Tram Museum, and, later, walking down Sauchiehall Street to explore some of the shops.

When Ben arrived in the early evening, Jenny liked the look of him immediately, and suggested they went off for a meal, just the two of them.

"Thanks to your coming, Ben," Jenny told him with a twinkle, "I can admit to feeling tired and wanting to turn in early!"

After only the briefest of arguments about it, the two young people walked away.

"She must be worn out," Sarah said. "What a day we've had, and we've walked miles — it's all been so marvellously exciting."

"Know what?" Ben said with a grin. "Your aunt could go on and walk a few more miles. She's not at all tired — she's just not going to play gooseberry!"

He was right. Jenny wasn't tired, but she did have a lot to think about, and she wanted to write to Mary in Aberdeen.

SHE was wide awake when Sarah came in to kiss her good night and tell her everything was wonderful.

Jenny didn't mention the next day, but she had already decided she must leave the young people to themselves to do whatever they wanted.

Only, the two young people wouldn't hear of it.

"Were *all* going to Luss, like you said," Sarah told her firmly at breakfast, and then added with a teasing twinkle, "Of course, Ben and I will probably go for a walk along the loch while you have your afternoon nap!"

"How dare you!" But Jenny was laughing. "I tell you what . . ."

But what Jenny was going to tell them never got said because at that moment, the waitress told her that there was someone to see her in the hall . . .

When she went through to reception, Malcolm Craigie was waiting.

"Hello," he said warmly, shaking Jenny's hand. "I just came to tell you I phoned Mary last night and she wants you to ring her, too, and go as soon as you can . . ."

Sounds

I'VE heard a thousand sounds today:
Birds singing at the dawn
A song of joy and ecstasy,
For the dark night had gone.

I heard the postman's footsteps ring,
Hurrying on his way,
Whistling a merry gladsome tune,
To greet the bright new day.

I heard the sleepy household stir —
Each dear familiar sound;
The clink of bottles on the step —
The milkman on his round.

I heard the children's bantering,
Their feet upon the stair;
And at the pressing of a switch
Sweet music filled the air.

I heard the April raindrops fall,
Soft wind among the trees;
And did I hear the cuckoo call
Across the woodland breeze?

I heard the traffic rumbling past,
Along the busy street;
I heard my close companion talk
As only he can speak.

He walks beside me every day
And never lags behind.
He is my faithful guide dog, Friend —
My eyes — for I am blind.
— *Patricia McGavock.*

"Oh! How wonderful," Jenny said excitedly. "And how good of you to come and tell me — to take the trouble."

Malcolm laughed.

"Well, actually, I didn't only come for that. I came for two other things. Firstly, would you let me drive you and your niece to Luss today? Please — it would give me so much pleasure!"

"That sounds marvellous," Jenny said with enthusiasm, "except that now, well, there's Sarah's boyfriend."

"Ah! He's arrived, has he? I rather guessed something was in the wind yesterday. Well where are they? Let's ask them."

The two young people were delighted at the prospect.

"Just as long as we're back in time for me to escort this young lady back home tonight," Ben said, "and myself back to the office at nine tomorrow!"

★   ★   ★   ★

It was later, after lunch, as Sarah and Ben started off for their walk, that Ben looked back.

"Do you know something, Sarah? I reckon now we're the ones who are being careful not to play gooseberry."

Sarah laughed incredulously, as she, too, looked back and waved at the couple on the balcony.

"Don't be ridiculous . . . not at their age!"

Ben kissed her firmly. "Mark my words, there's a miracle in the making . . ."

And who knows? Maybe he'll be proved to be right . . .

Because as they waved back to the young people, Jenny was saying to Malcolm, "When you arrived at the hotel this morning you said you'd come for two things. One was to drive us to Luss. What was the other?"

"Oh, that," he said, trying to sound offhand. "Well, I was due to go and see Mary shortly and she . . . I . . . I wondered whether we could fix it up at the same time. I could drive you to Aberdeen. It would be a lovely trip. It's a long way, but we could stop off to admire the view!"

It took Jenny a few moments to reply.

"Oh, Malcolm," she said at last, "that sounds a wonderful idea . . . and it will be so marvellous to see Mary."

And Malcolm Craigie was sighing with relief, for it had been many years since he'd asked anyone to go anywhere with him. He'd been scared, half-expecting he might at best be misunderstood, at worst be snubbed.

But Jenny's delight banished such fears.

Further down the loch, Sarah was saying musingly to Ben, "I wonder if Malcolm drove us back to the hotel yesterday so he could find out where we were staying . . . if he didn't like to ask."

Ben laughed and hugged her.

"You're coming on nicely!" he teased. ☐

WEDNESDAY, 10.30 a.m. I was sat at our white deal table in our — well now, my — over-big kitchen.

At 10.30 a.m., ever since Mother died, six years ago, Daddy and I had sat with elbows on the table and our hands round two large mugs, drinking our morning cuppa.

Today was Wednesday. Daddy wasn't sat opposite as he had passed away last week, and after the funeral I was on my own in our large Victorian house in Moffat.

What did the future hold? I was twenty-seven, unmarried and had no professional training. Daddy didn't agree with girls going out to work.

The Antique
~Collectors~
by Mary Gorst

I knew that I had no need to worry from the financial side. Daddy had made good but I couldn't just rattle about for the rest of my life in this big house.

What should I do?

I never got round to answering this question as the phone rang.

The outside world had remembered I was alive. I picked it up and before I could ask who was ringing, a voice said cheerfully:

"Hey — you are depressed. Must do something about that."

I knew from the very pleasant, round Cumbrian voice who was on the other end. None other than Auntie Alice from Kendal.

"I'm just doing carrots, onions, potatoes. Would you rather have a beef or lamb hot-pot?"

I laughed, the first time for over a week. You couldn't help it with Auntie Alice from Kendal.

"Beef."

"Right. I'll have it ready for five and you'll be there."

She went chatting on. She knew I would be lonely and wanted me to come down and buck her up as well.

She, like me, had stayed with her parents. To my knowledge she'd had two proposals of marriage but said sorry and stayed with her folk. Now, like mine, they were no more.

She was some far distant relation of my father's. I guess a forty-second cousin, age forty-two or thereby. Round, jolly and enjoyed life.

When she said she would have her hot-pot ready for five she knew I would come down the motorway from Moffat and turn off for Kendal at Crooklands in no time.

Needless to say, I packed a few things, threw them in the back of my MG — a present from Dad — called at the bank and headed south.

I turned off the motorway at Penrith, had a snack at the hotel just south of the humped-back bridge on the corner where the road branches west for Ullswater at Eamont.

It was a bright, late April day. Instead of going back on to the motorway and the rat race, I went down the good old A6. That was the way we always went before the motorway was built and so did thousands of others.

I met, in all, five cars coming from the South and the driver of each waved as though we were lost souls crossing the Sahara.

Alice was as good as her word, a typical Cumbrian high tea was awaiting me. We chatted well into the night about, I'm afraid, the future. We went to bed without solving the problem.

O N Thursday, Alice, who was always a good organiser, stated we were going to Kirkby Lonsdale for a walk down to and over the famous Devil's Bridge, and then a bar lunch at the hotel in the square.

Kirkby Lonsdale is a fascinating old market town, stone, harl and slates — plus the famous bridge.

"Look, there's an auction sale." Alice saw the notice as we went down the hill into the square.

Mother and I used to attend any house furniture sale that was held within ten miles of Moffat.

I loved good furniture, so did Mother.

Alice and I forgot Devil's Bridge. Into the saleroom we went but only had ten minutes to look round the items on offer before the sale began.

It was, we soon saw by the items, a very high-class sale of antique furniture.

We watched with interest as the items were held aloft and then the spirited bidding.

"Ladies and gentlemen. Item thirty-eight. Library steps. Beautiful condition. Who'll start me at sixty pounds? No bids. Fifty, then?"

"Forty-five I'm bid. Thank you, sir. It's a start."

"Fifty pounds at the back."

"Fifty-five. Thank you, madam."

"Sixty."

"Madam, the bid is against you."

Alice gave me a dig in the side.

"He's speaking to you."

I didn't need her to tell me. I knew.

I bid again. A gentleman standing at the side smiled and didn't bid again.

"The lady on the third row."

A boy came for my name and address.

"What is it?"

"Library steps."

I could see Alice thought I had gone mad.

We left shortly afterwards, paid for my "mad buy" — Alice's words — and took it to the car.

I'd always been intrigued by that centre pole, with its three spiral steps leading nowhere, but never thought I would own a set.

We went for lunch. Alice still thought I was mad. I hadn't a library, so why buy library steps?

It's difficult to explain why you rashly go on bidding for something just because you like it.

As I "had money to burn" — Alice's statement — I could pay for the lunch.

▶ *p108*

LONG dubbed — The Capital of the Highlands, Inverness is a historic town situated on the River Ness. J. Campbell Kerr's painting, overleaf, captures the difference between old and new. The up-to-date shopping centre on the riverbank contrasts starkly with the old castle on the hill. Inverness Castle is relatively modern, however, as castles go, but carved stones, burial stones and hilltop fort remain to prove that the site was inhabited long before written historical records. Inverness is steeped in history, and names like King Duncan, Malcolm III, Robert the Bruce, King Edward I of England and Mary, Queen of Scots, are all part of the history of Inverness.

The present castle was put up in two parts — in 1834 and 1846 and, unlike its predecessors, it hasn't figured in battles and uprisings. It is used, quite simply, as the Sheriff Court House and administrative office.

INVERNESS, Highland Region : J CAMPBELL KERR

On the Friday I suggested a run through to Keswick.

We had coffee and scones by the waterside at Ambleside.

In Keswick we parked the car and walked up the street to the open market by the old town hall.

We walked towards the Royal Oak for lunch. Alice saw a skirt she fancied and dived into the shop. I wasn't skirt-minded so walked on.

Two doors up was an antique shop. I went inside.

"A young man, well, a man about my own age, came forward and nodded pleasantly.

"Good morning, miss, you got a bargain in your library steps yesterday."

I looked at him, so he told me later, with a blank look.

"I stopped bidding when I saw you wanted them."

He had been at the sale at Kirkby Lonsdale.

I then remembered he was the gentleman that had smiled and not bid again.

I thanked him and, so I was told, blushed.

He asked if I had a library.

"No, I just liked them. I am interested in old furniture."

He took me round his front and back shop showing me beautiful pieces of furniture, china and silverware.

There was a small square box on a long handle on the wall just as we went into his back shop.

I asked its use — the reason being I had seen one years ago.

MUM and Dad didn't go abroad for their holidays, in fact they didn't go far at all.

I was about fifteen and we were taking our summer holiday at the Borrowdale Hotel which is a few miles down the side of Derwentwater from Keswick.

We had taken a run to the village of Grange, a mile to the south.

Just over the beautiful stone bridge is a church.

Dad was always interested in churches. The door was open and we went in. I don't remember much about the church but I will always remember examining the two boxes on long handles on the back seat. They intrigued me.

Here, in this antique shop in Keswick, was one of these boxes.

"By the way, my name is Eric Halton."

Mr Halton went on to explain that in churches, in sheep areas, shepherds brought their dogs to church. They sat under the pew and it was thought advisable to pass the plate rather than risk a bite from a fed-up dog. And that what the little box on the end of the long handle really was.

I asked the price and agreed to buy.

"Do you have your own antique business?"

As he asked that simple question something clicked inside me. The answer to my question, "What did the future hold?"

"Not yet, but I hope to have one going in three months."

"Good. I'll give you a dealer's discount on your collection box."
I sat down at his desk and made out a cheque.

He handed me his card and asked for my address in Moffat (he got that from the cheque) as he would like to be my first customer.

I thanked him and left, clutching my long-handled collection box.

Alice was sure I had got knocked down and taken to the local hospital.

"Alice, we are going to the Borrowdale Hotel for a celebration lunch and it's on me."

"What's that you've bought?"

"Never mind — it's a beginning."

"A beginning of what?"

Poor Alice was all at sea, and looking back I don't wonder.

"If I didn't know you I'd say by the glint in your eye you were in love."

"Don't be daft. In love with a collection box."

We had a dry sherry before lunch. I ordered a half bottle of Barsac to be served with our meal so that we could celebrate.

We were enjoying this treat when out of the blue a young gentleman was standing by our table.

"Miss Calton, if I'd known you were coming here for lunch I would have asked you to be my guest. Will you two join me for coffee after?"

I made the introductions.

"Alice, this is Eric Halton who is going to come and advise me about my antique venture. Alice is coming to help me."

"Pleased to meet you, Alice. See you later, Miss Calton."

"How long have you known Eric?"

"An hour."

"You are a quick worker. What's this about an antique business and me helping?"

I had to explain to Alice that I had decided to go into the antique business in Moffat and I wanted her to come and live with me and help.

"Are you going to have a shop?"

"No, but I want to discuss my ideas with Mr Halton."

"You mean Eric?" She gave me such a look. She said I blushed.

O VER coffee I explained to Mr Halton — otherwise Eric — about my dad having left me with a big house full of beautiful furniture. How the lounge and dining-room lead off the hall and these would be my display rooms plus the hall.

Oh no, you couldn't just walk in, I explained. No, ring the bell or by appointment only.

Alice was all agog.

Could he come through the following Wednesday and see my house? He was going to a sale at Tweedsmuir. Would I like to go with him?

There was only one answer — or rather two. I would be delighted if he would come and give me advice about my house as an antique display centre.

Alice drove back to Kendal. She maintained I was up in the clouds and would kill us both before we even got to Ambleside.

In a more sober mood that evening as we sat at Alice's kitchen table with a mug of cocoa, I explained in more detail what I had in mind.

Alice jumped at the idea though she looked thoughtful.

"What happens to me if you get wed?"

"What a hope at my age!"

"How old's Eric? He isn't married?"

Alice said I blushed again.

I got planning permission for a change of use from house to antique show house.

Mr Halton — Eric — came to see it, made certain suggestions and then whisked me off to the sale in Tweedsmuir.

We both bought but never bid against each other.

I enjoyed the day. We had lunch at a hotel nearby.

The Manor House Antiques at Moffat flourished. Alice looked after the shop as it were, when I went to sales — often with Eric.

I must be slow. One day at a sale in Carlisle an antique dealer I knew by sight came over and chatted.

He came from Kendal and must have called at the Manor House and met Alice.

"Miss Calton, you have a very helpful assistant at Moffat."

I thanked him and said I would pass his kind remarks on to Alice.

Alice blushed when I told her. How was I to know he had often called when he knew I would be at a sale?

"Alice, what'll I do if *you* get married?"

"Get married."

I had to laugh at her quick off-the-cuff answer.

She was right. Eric and I did get married, lived in Moffat. He put someone in the Keswick shop and went down two or three times a week.

Alice is living "over the shop" as it were, at an antique shop in Kendal, very very happy with her Ewan.

We are going in three weeks' time to have a celebration dinner at the Borrowdale Hotel. We will have been married five years then. As Eric says, if I hadn't, for no reason at all, bought those library steps he would never have met me. I haven't sold them. Neither have I sold the wooden collection box with a long handle.

They are too precious to turn into silver. □

SITUATED near Bromyard in Worcestershire, Brockhampton Hall is a fascinating glimpse at the past. It's a half-timbered 14th century house with a rare 15th century gatehouse over the surrounding moat. The house and gatehouse are cared for by the National Trust.

BROCKHAMPTON HALL and GATE HOUSE : J CAMPBELL KERR

A YOUNG FOOLISH

AND HEART

UNTIL that morning, Irene had hoped that Ted Graham was beginning to see her as something more than just one of the "gang" who met daily in the firm's canteen for lunch, and sometimes at the sports club in the evenings.

Twice lately, he had suggested they take lunch-time sandwiches to the park, just about half a mile from the big store where she worked in the boutique section, and he in the accounts.

Some of the others would tease Ted sometimes about being "old fashioned." But to Irene, he was everything she admired and looked for in a man.

It had nothing to do with the fact that he was handsome, and tall and tough. It had everything to do with the fact that he was kind and human, with a gorgeous sense of humour and

**by
KATE
MORTIMER**

was knowledgeable about so many things.

But after Andrea, his schoolgirl sister, had poured out her heart while buying the green blouse for her special date, Irene was uneasy — an unease which grew into a terrible fear for Andrea, and doubt about how to act.

Little did the girl realise, that with every word she uttered, she was bringing the past back to Irene — a past she had so resolutely put behind her two years ago.

Now, she had to face it again.

Andrea had been into the boutique section a couple of times during the past month, once to buy a belt, and once a scarf. Irene had realised at once she was Ted's sister because they were so alike — they had different coloured hair but the same dark, sparkling eyes and sensitive mouth.

H

She'd also realised that Andrea was glowing with excitement.

"I want a gorgeous blouse," she said, her eyes sparkling and her cheeks flushed, "for a very special date. It's to wear with a long black skirt."

Irene knew it was the school's half-term holiday, and that next week there was to be a big celebration of its foundation two hundred years ago. Now it was the most famous school in the county town of Benton.

"I've got just the one for you," she told Andrea enthusiastically. "A dream — in emerald green."

Andrea was enchanted with it, pirouetting round the boutique, looking at it from every angle.

"It's gorgeous," she cried and then laughed, "what a difference from that one!" looking at her school uniform blouse dropped on to one of the golden chairs.

Irene, pleased with her delight, told her then, "You will be the belle of the school party. See how the boys will come running!"

BUT as she spoke, Irene saw the girl's expression change into what her mother used to call "an old-fashioned look," when a child was going to prevaricate.

"Oh! It's not for the school party," Andrea said with scorn, as she stroked the blouse gleefully, "It's for . . . for . . . well, a wonderful date with a special . . . friend."

Ah, well, Irene thought with inward amusement, girls did start dating boys at 16 — or even before.

"How exciting," she said lightly, "well, you'll certainly impress him with *that*."

"He's worth impressing." Andrea laughed, her voice rather shrill then. "He's marvellous, over six feet tall, gorgeously good looking and clever. I'm crazy about him — you know the feeling!"

"Yes," Irene said, "I know the feeling." But at that moment alarm bells began to ring. Was she really describing a schoolboy?

As if floodgates were unleashed, Andrea poured out the story about how she'd met this wonderful man at the Royalty Disco; how he travelled; how he was going to take her to London, and sometime to Paris. And then she said it: "Isn't it strange, he's such a Samson of a man and his name is actually Samson. I must say it suits him no end!"

Samson! It couldn't be, Irene told herself, it just couldn't be.

But from that moment she knew that it *was* Brian Samson, the Brian she had met two years ago when she was 18.

Her brain whirring, somehow Irene forced herself to say lightly, "He does sound impressive," and then she added casually, "does he get on well with . . . with your family?"

"My family!" Andrea laughed shrilly. "Oh, they don't know. Mum and Dad, anyway, are up in Scotland looking after my aunt who is ill. But they and my brothers would say he's too old, and he isn't — he's just about thirty. Some time I'll take him home. But not yet . . ."

Andrea laughed again. "Oh, I bet *you* kept secrets from your parents."

Irene hesitated, then said, "Yes — and lived to regret it. You see . . ."

But Andrea interrupted her, clearly in no mood to listen to any warning, veiled or not. She had to rush off, she said, she had an appointment now due, at the hairdresser's.

And anyway, Irene thought, watching her rush away, nothing she could ever say would, *could*, do anything.

She shivered, remembering how little notice *she* had taken of hints and warnings when she was in love, for the first time in her life with the wonderful Brian Samson.

No, it needed something more than words to save Andrea Graham from herself. But what?

Irene loathed interfering busybodies but she couldn't just stand by and let a girl like Andrea head for disaster.

SOMEHOW, Irene got through the rest of the morning, but when she went to the canteen at lunchtime, she only wanted a cup of coffee. For the life of her, she couldn't have eaten anything.

"What on earth is wrong?" Ted said at once, when he came over to her table. "You look . . . as if something awful has happened."

"It has," Jill tried to speak calmly, "but not to me. It's just that . . . I'm dreadfully worried about . . ."

Instantly, Ted stood up. "Trouble shared is trouble halved. Look, I'll get some sandwiches and we'll have them in the park. No, I'll have no arguments."

He took her arm resolutely, and a few minutes later they were sitting on deckchairs in the park.

"Now, come on, let me help — whatever it is," Ted said quietly, but with a voice full of kindness and warmth.

"I . . . I can't," Irene said unsteadily. How could she reveal Andrea's confidences to the girl's brother? "It's . . . it's not really my . . . I can't talk about someone else's affairs. I . . ."

Ted leaned forward, took her hands and looked straight at her. "Look, you needn't tell me any names. Just tell me what the problem is . . ."

For a long time Irene didn't answer, and he didn't try to hurry her.

Then at last she said, "It's just that . . . a young friend of mine has fallen for someone I know is . . ."

"Married?" Ted said quietly.

"Yes, with two children . . . and . . ." Swiftly, Irene explained that it wasn't only that; that he was taking the girl to doubtful places; that he was proposing to take her to London . . . to Paris . . .

"Evidently, you *are* sure about this man?"

"Yes, I'm sure . . ." Irene's voice broke, and again she was silent for a while. But she knew there was only one way of justifying her apparent interference with her un-named "friend," without looking like a gossiping busybody.

So, briefly, quickly and, she knew, inadequately, she told Ted Graham how and why she was so sure.

"I was . . . sort of lucky," she went on. "I was older, and I found out in time." So she told him about the day Brian's wife had gone to see her, and spoken of their children.

"She was . . . is a nice girl. She was nice to me. But . . ." Irene shivered ". . . the humiliation was awful! I . . . I'd hate this schoolgirl to have that happen to her."

Her voice broke off and she couldn't say another word.

WHEN Ted spoke, his voice was so cool and steely that Irene hardly recognised it.

"Now I'll tell you something, Irene," he said. "My parents are away, and for a while I've been very worried about my sister. She's been in some strange moods, sometimes almost hysterical. She's been getting a lot of letters, coming home late and behaving very oddly."

He hesitated a moment, and then went on steadily. "I . . . I know you would never betray a confidence — and I don't want you to. But, Irene, I know Andrea was coming to the store today to buy a blouse — Dad had given her the money for it and it's supposed to be for the big school party."

He turned to her.

"Irene, this is something a man has to handle, and that man must be me — never mind who the girl is. So please will you give me his name and address?"

In a voice shaking with shock, Irene told him. Then, in absolute silence, they walked back to the store.

★　　　★　　　★　　　★

"And that's the end for me," she told herself as she walked home to her little apartment that night, remembering that cold, steely voice.

Obviously, he had been deeply shocked by what she had told him. And . . . well, as the others had said so often, Ted was the old-fashioned type.

But one thing was in no doubt, he'd know how to handle Brian Samson so that Andrea would never know exactly what had happened. He would see to it that Brian never saw his sister again.

As for me, Irene thought, *I won't be seeing Ted for much longer either. I must get another job. I couldn't bear to see those cold, unfriendly eyes every day . . .*

One thing she could do, she thought with a wry smile, was to ring her parents at her father's farm. Reassured by her dad's steady "You did quite right, love. The only thing that matters is saving that young girl from herself and that dreadful character!" Irene made herself a cup of coffee.

The bell rang, and a voice called out through the letterbox:

"It's me. Ted Graham."

A Young And Foolish Heart

Oh, no! Irene thought. I can't bear any more.

He strode into the tiny living-room with the purposeful air of a man who has got everything under control.

He stood, leaning against the bookshelves, and told her, "I've seen him, and made him write a letter, a *nice* letter, saying his conscience was pricking him . . . I've got it in my pocket and it will be in the letterbox at our house tomorrow morning. Then I shall be around if Andrea needs a shoulder to cry on.

"In fact, I wouldn't be surprised if now, she tells me all about it." He looked at Irene. "So you don't need to look so . . . upset. You've made a miracle and . . . do I smell coffee?" ▶ *over*

★ PARTNERQUOTES ★

BACALL

1967: She left her own tribute to Bogie at his funeral. It was the immortal line from their first film together. *"If you want anything, just whistle . . ."*
1972: *"Marriage always came first with me. I have always put my man before anything else."*
1976: *"I'm very naive about men. I always have been. I trust them, and I don't expect to be let down."*
Timeless: *"I was in love with a wonderful man, and he was in love with me . . ."*

BOGART

1940s: *"Quit asking me whether or not I was drunk. It's my business if I want to buy a couple of pandas a drink!"*
On meeting Frank Sinatra for the first time: *"They tell me you have a voice that makes girls faint. Make me faint."*
1945: *"I had to marry her. She chased me until I had my back to the wall. I did what any gentleman would do. I acquiesced . . ."*
Timeless: *"If you want your coat held then don't try to act like a feller . . ."*

HUMPHREY BOGART & LAUREN BACALL — PARTNERS FOR EVER

117

"Yes," Irene said tautly. She went into the kitchen and took another cup from the dresser, irritated because Ted followed her and sat down at the small table.

NOW it was all over, she wanted to be alone. Hoping that Ted would soon go now, she murmured, "You can't . . . you mustn't be too sure of her reaction."

"I think I can," he said, slowly sipping the coffee. "It's such a relief that it's done without anything . . . well, anything drastic," he went on. "But I did of course hint to Samson what can be done with a man who takes out schoolgirls."

There was a silence, and then he said, "I'm so horrified, Irene, that because of Andrea, *you* had to . . . well you decided you had to . . . talk about what happened to you. It must have been a terribly difficult thing for you to do. It all added to my fury with Samson!"

Again he leaned forward, as he had done that day in the park, and gripped both her hands. "I don't know how you found the courage to do it. But I will always be eternally grateful."

"Grateful?" Irene murmured, bemused. "I . . . I thought you . . . that you were most horribly shocked."

Ted laughed. "Shocked? Me? You silly girl. How could I be, when you were merely proving what I was beginning to think — that you're a wonderful girl."

"But, Ted, you . . . well I thought . . . after all, you know you are a bit old fashioned about girls. And such a revelation from me, I thought . . ."

"You idiot!" he cried. "I'll tell you why I'm old fashioned about girls. It's because a few years ago I made a fool of myself over someone who just wasn't worth it. Oh, Irene, don't you realise that we all make fools of ourselves at least once when we're young?"

He stood up abruptly. "Have you eaten — no, of course you haven't. Shall we dine out or . . ."

"I don't feel I could cope with going out," Irene told him, beginning to feel that the earth was falling away from her feet.

"Then could we raid your fridge, and eat what we fancy? Would you mind?"

"No," Irene said. "I wouldn't mind at all."

So, she made omelettes as Ted kept the conversation firmly away from events of that day, and talked of tennis, holidays, walks on the moors.

It was only when he was going that Irene said, "I do hope you're right . . . but I'm still afraid."

Ted put his hands on her shoulders, and kissed her gently.

"Believe me, it will be all right," he whispered. "Andrea is destined for a new beginning and . . . and so are we."

He turned back from the open door. "I wouldn't mind betting that Andrea will be back at the boutique to change her blouse — in a flaming temper!"

JUST after nine o'clock, Andrea swept in to the boutique, eyes blazing, and asked if she could change the blouse.

"Of course," Irene said calmly, "but I'm sorry you don't like it."

It was in the cubicle, trying on another blouse, that Andrea told her about the letter. Thankfully, Irene realised that her pride was hurt much more than her heart.

"Oh, not to worry," Irene said blithely, remembering Ted's words. "It happens to us all. And we all have to realise it isn't the end of the world."

Andrea looked at her. "Have you ever been . . . disillusioned by a man?"

"Oh sure," Irene said. "I tried to tell you yesterday but you wouldn't listen. Nor did I, at the time!"

After she had chosen a soft, silky, yellow blouse, Andrea said,

---

My Feathered Friends

IT'S quiet by my desk, alone,
  Watching birds fly to yonder tree.
I know not if they call this home,
  Nor they how their flight pleaseth me.

Bright colours are those feathered friends
  Who feed upon my cast-out bread.
They wash and preen as each day ends,
  Take wing and fly off home to bed.

Will they return to seek my food,
  Sing to me by my window sill?
Oh, modest friends, your world is good —
  You do not fear the paws that kill.

You'll fly far from the winter's chill
  In far-off, foreign lands to sing.
Yet next year I'll be waiting still
  To welcome you home in the spring.
                              — H. F. Molesworth.

"My brother, Ted, was having his breakfast when I found the letter. I cried all over him, and then I felt better."

"Good," Irene said, "nothing like a sturdy shoulder."

"He's said he'll take me to London, to that big pop concert at the Albert Hall. Won't it be smashing?"

"Lucky you," Irene said. "It will indeed."

Andrea looked at her thoughtfully for a moment and then said suddenly, "He said I could bring a friend. Would you like to come — you've been such an angel listening to all my nattering."

Irene laughed. "But he would mean a school friend."

"Why? Look," Andrea said enthusiastically, forgetting her raging temper with Brian Samson, "it would be wonderful. And I'm sure you'd like him. Actually, he works in this store, on the top floor."

Irene put her hands on the girl's shoulders. "I'll leave it all to you. I'd love to come, but you'd better ask your brother first."

Andrea beamed. "I will. Come to think of it," she said, "he could do with a nice girlfriend!" □

A Message

by MARY LEDGWAY

I SWITCHED on the television and, tucking my slim legs under me, settled back with my coffee.

I hadn't looked to see what was on — I knew I would just catch the end of "Songs Of Praise" — but I was totally unprepared to see the small church where I had worshipped throughout my years of growing up.

With one swift movement I knelt in front of the screen, wondering if there would be a familiar face, but it was over thirty years since I had moved to Yorkshire and the cameras moved quickly.

Just as the congregation were fading away, though, I tensed. It couldn't be! It was!

Without any doubts it was Katie Kennedy standing there, her hymn book lowered, singing the words of the old hymn with the same fervour she had done all those years before.

Then the sound faded and the credits came on. I switched the set off and went back to my seat, but I was no longer aware of the comforts of my small cottage sitting-room. I was a child again . . .

I saw again the wild country of Donegal. I was tramping over the fields on our three-mile walk to school, and as always urging my sister, Bridie, to hurry. There was barely a year between us, but we were completely different in appearance and temperament.

I, Margaret McGregor, small and delicately built, loved school. Bridie, well made and proud of her strength, hated it.

On the days when our father decreed it was too wet or snowy for us to make the long walk to the small school, I would be unable to stem my tears. Bridie, on the other hand, would shout aloud with glee.

When we were allowed to make our way through the damp and mists that so often prevailed, the teacher, Bessie Green, small in stature but big and cuddly in all other aspects, would greet us with mugs of hot chocolate, and let us dry our cold feet by the wood-burning stove.

120

From Teacher

Sitting in my quiet sitting-room, I relived it all. Bessie Bunter, as she was affectionately known, was more concerned with making sure her twenty charges were happy and smiling than in their standard of education.

I did Bridie's homework for her with unfailing regularity. Bessie passed it back, duly marked, and said nothing. In return Bridie would wheel my cycle over the rough ground, take the biggest half of the kitchen floor when it was our turn to scrub it, and carry my books for me when I was tired.

The arrangement worked well — until Katie Kennedy arrived.

══════════════*A Helping Hand*══════════════

WHO are the members of the team
    Who seldom with their
  colleagues meet,
Who do their daily stint removed
  From office workers, warm and
    neat?
Home helps.

Who trot about with hurried gait,
  With household problems on their
    minds,
To oil the wheels of life for those
  Whose active days are left behind?
Home helps.

Who comfort bring when pain is all
  And busy kin have failed to call?
Summon help and reassure
  When feeble limbs have caused a
    fall?
Home helps.

Who proffer willing feet and hands
  To fetch the pension, shop or cook?
Make the tea and feed the cat,
  And hunt for knitting, specs' or
    book?
Home helps.

Who listen not with pencil poised,
  But duster brisk at household chore,
To tales of sorrow joy or pain
  They've heard a hundred times
    before?
Home helps.

While social scientists advise,
  Their learned theories try to prove,
Who, caring, puts them to the test
  In daily acts of Christian love?
Home helps.

— A. E. Belton.

WE were returning to school after the long summer break. Occasionally our dad's young brother — born when Dad was already a married man — Uncle Johnnie, would give us a lift on his cart. We would pick other children up on the way and sit singing the old Irish songs as we jolted through the country lanes.

That's how it was that first morning — the morning we met Katie.

Johnnie took the cart through the gates of the tiny, concrete playground, and we all stared when a small whirlwind approached him telling Johnnie in no uncertain terms to get the horse out of there.

"But — I always bring Benny in. He's perfectly harmless."

"Harmless he might be — but the children have to play here. What if . . . ?"

Katie Kennedy blushed and Johnnie burst out laughing as he

stepped down to haul the children out. He turned to Miss Kennedy. "Oh, not to worry, ma'am! If Benny dares to do anything like that I have a shovel handy."

We children, brought up to the ways of nature, were all giggling and Katie Kennedy glared at Johnnie Macpherson as, inevitably, the worst happened.

"And who might you be?" he asked as he obligingly reached for the shovel. "Where's our dear old Bessie?"

"I'm *Miss* Kennedy!" he was told haughtily. "Miss Green was unwell during the holidays and has gone to live with her sister."

With this, she tugged at the old bell rope and rang the bell loud and clear — something Bessie Bunter had never bothered with. The few children scattered about were so startled they ran into line and without a backward glance at our uncle, Miss Kennedy marched them into the single classroom.

I did manage to glance back at Uncle Johnnie and saw him looking after Katie Kennedy with a strange expression in his laughing Irish eyes. It was not my imagination either, when Katie Kennedy's face softened as she walked over to the window, ostensibly for paper, but in time to watch the cart being driven out through the gates.

We soon found that school under Katie Kennedy was very different from a school run by Bessie Bunter.

There was no hot chocolate, although she did warm our morning milk. If we wanted to dry our feet by the comfort of the stove we had to be there before nine o'clock to do it. Lessons began at nine, and nothing was allowed to interfere.

Bessie would often send us out of school early.

"You've all a long walk in front of you."

But only if the weather threatened to turn nasty did Katie allow such a thing. And not always then!

At first, she was unused to the quick changes in the Irish weather but after a few worrying times when some of the children were caught in the mist, she learnt to ask some of the older children and followed their advice.

DESPITE the changes, I began to love the new order of things. Miss Kennedy kept pace with each child's work individually and even turned a small storage room into a spare room for private study. There was a "no talking" rule though and most of the other children avoided it.

I was one of the few to use it as much as I was allowed. As Miss Kennedy checked each person's homework carefully, though, I feared for Bridie.

For the first week of the term I was careful to make hers different from mine — a few sums wrong, a different subject for composition, as we called it.

Then came the time I was not well. I insisted on doing my homework before Mother packed me off to bed early and was soon asleep.

123

The next day Miss Kennedy called both Bridie and me to her desk. My heart sank when I saw the books laid out on the table.

"Bridie," she said quietly, "show me how you worked these figures out."

Bridie stared at the blank sheet of paper, and shook her head.

"So you did copy from Margaret. You should both know —"

"Margaret was in bed! She didn't know!" Bridie told her fiercely. "I can't do —"

"In future," interrupted Miss Kennedy sternly, "you will both have different exercises. And from now on if I catch you copying, Bridie, or Margaret helping you, it will mean the cane. That is all for now."

Bridie was furious, but secretly I was a little relieved. I knew Miss Kennedy was pleased with my work and now I could leap ahead without worrying about Bridie. But Bridie didn't forget, and the extra time she had to spend struggling with her own work made her dislike poor Katie Kennedy even more.

I DON'T think Bridie ever noticed how often Uncle Johnnie took us to school that term. Or that he managed on several occasions to call to take us home on his cart. After that first day he always left Benny outside the school.

Uncle Johnnie had a smallholding of his own but worked for a local farmer as well, so he didn't have a lot of spare time.

It was funny how Bridie, a year older than me, missed seeing how Katie Kennedy's face lit up when Johnnie came walking through the gates. He would laughingly tell us to go and climb aboard and the time we had to wait for him grew longer and longer as he talked to Katie.

And there was that light in their eyes. I saw how he would touch her hand, her heightened colour when he told her her dress was the same colour as her eyes, and I suspected many a walk by the sea, or trip into the country at the weekends.

Knowing how Bridie fe!*, though, I said nothing. But the thought of having Katie Kennedy in the family gave me a warm feeling.

Then, three weeks before the end of term, Johnnie's boss was taken ill and he had to run both farms. Whether he contacted Katie or not, I don't know, but at the weekend she slipped a letter into my hand.

"Please, Margaret. Will you see your Uncle Johnnie gets it?"

I nodded, proud at being asked, yet knowing why she had asked me and not Bridie. She knew Bridie didn't like her.

On the way home, though, Bridie spotted the letter peeping out of my pocket. I had to tell her what it was, and before I could stop her she snatched the letter and tore it across and across, scattering the pieces over the wooden bridge into the stream.

I was horrified and burst into tears, but my sister only laughed.

"The sooner that little affair is nipped in the bud, the better."

Although she was only eleven she sounded much older. The letter

A Message From Teacher

had gone and there was nothing I could do — but what would I be able to say when Katie Kennedy asked me about it?

As it happened she never did. The weather was bad and for the next few days snow kept us at home. I developed a cold and had two more days off while Bridie trudged reluctantly to school.

The only thing Miss Kennedy said to me was, "Do you have a letter for me?"

I COULD only shake my head. I wanted to tell her about Uncle Johnnie having to work all hours, but the look in her eyes when there was no letter brought such a lump into my throat I couldn't speak. By the time I could, Katie was at her desk talking to the class about Christmas.

I was also reluctant to tell on Bridie.　▶ *over*

PARTNERQUOTES

RICHARD BURTON
Timeless: *"I love the woman. We were together for twenty years. She will always be a part of me and I will always be a part of her."*

LIZ TAYLOR
1986: *"No matter what happens, I'm loud, noisy, earthy and ready for much more living."*
1986: *"Not only did I love him, but I loved to work with him, too."*
1986: *"He was generous to a glorious degree . . ."*

RICHARD BURTON & LIZ TAYLOR — A CONSUMING PASSION

THE next term Katie wasn't there. Only then did we learn that she had come to us to regain her strength after an illness. That she had taught underprivileged children in a large city school. Her successor was good, but I still grieved after Katie Kennedy.

When I was sixteen I left home and came to Yorkshire to train as a children's nurse. After a while, Bridie followed me to work in a hotel. Eventually she married the son of the house and made an ideal publican's wife. Bright and breezy, her long dark hair and dark brown eyes as attractive as ever, she was happy and her lack of learning didn't worry anyone.

I passed all my exams and went on to be a tutor to the young nurses. The children I watched over were my life. Slowly I paid for my little cottage and was content. Bridie's three children visited often and I was never lonely.

Oh! I nearly forgot to mention that Johnnie's boss died soon after I came to Yorkshire and left him some money. He sold his own farm and bought a sheep farm on the dales.

Before he left Ireland I travelled to Donegal to see him married to Ruth Brady, a local lassie who had been at school before Katie's brief reign. As I watched, though, I couldn't help thinking how Katie would have looked as the bride, and again I saw the pieces of the letter drifting away on the stream.

Ruth was a nice girl, but didn't settle in Yorkshire and ten years after their marriage she returned to Ireland, but their son, David, stayed with Johnnie. He had inherited his father's love of farming and Ruth realised it would not be fair to take him away from the life he loved.

Now Katie was back in Donegal! Why?

My reverie was disturbed then by the entrance of Bridie.

"What! All in the dark? You all right?" she asked as she flooded the room with light.

"Guess who I've just seen on 'Songs Of Praise' from Donegal? Katie Kennedy!"

I expected Bridie to make some witty remark about bad pennies but life had mellowed her and she looked a little sad.

"Remember the letter?" she asked. "I've often thought about it. I shouldn't have done it, Margaret. Katie did ask me if you had delivered it. You know, those two days I was at school without you, and I said yes. I couldn't tell her what I had done. I wish I had. Ruth didn't turn out to be a very good wife . . . Still, it's too late now."

But was it? I sat thinking after she had gone. Before I could change my mind I rang Johnnie and asked him to come over.

I told him about the letter, and suddenly there was the glint of tears in his eyes.

"Oh, Margaret, if I'd only known. Katie had told me she was going back to the city and I asked her to stay in Donegal and marry me. She said if I didn't hear from her I would know she had decided to return to her old job." Then, as Bridie had done, he added that it was too late now.

"But it needn't be," I said eagerly. "Katie's in Donegal. I've some holiday to come! We could go —"

"And find her married to someone else?"

"Perhaps, but perhaps not. Anyway, I'd like to see Donegal again."

THE sun was soft the evening Johnnie drove me to my old home. My cousins welcomed us and it was as though time had stood still. On Sunday evening we walked across to the small church, but Johnnie wouldn't come in.

"I'll go for a walk round. You will know what to say, if she is there!" he added with a smile.

Katie was there. She came and sat in the pew opposite me and when our eyes met I knew she recognised me. After the service she came across.

"Margaret! What a lovely surprise."

We talked a few minutes as she told me how she had decided to retire in the place she had grown fond of.

"And Johnnie?" she asked, not hiding her interest. I was grown up now.

"He didn't get your letter," I said as we walked out into the warmth of the sun.

"Oh, Margaret," she whispered.

Her eyes, gentle, older, were suddenly pools of pain. "Why didn't you tell me? I thought — "

Welcome Home

SUCH a flurry of excitement,
    Such a rushing to the door,
Barking dog, ecstatic children,
Smiling Granny to the fore!
All the house so bright and cheerful,
Bowl of roses in the hall,
Little faces clean and shining,
Touch of magic over all . . .
Smell of baking from the kitchen,
Washing blowing in the sun,
Thanks to Granny, up so early,
To make sure each job was done.

Sound of taxi-cab's departure,
Now the door is open wide,
Little voices call a greeting
As the loved ones step inside;
Daddy, with one arm encircling
Dearest Mum, who's been away
For two whole weeks — it seemed a lifetime!
Now she's home again, to stay.
But the centre of attraction,
Oh, so precious! Oh, so small!
Is the darling, brand-new baby,
Snuggled in the soft white shawl.

— *Kathleen O'Farrell.*

Then he was walking towards us and I knew at once the old magic was there. The extra forty years couldn't dim the love light in their eyes.

Their hands met, and I knew he would see, as I had done, that there was no ring on Katie's wedding finger. He drew her towards him. I couldn't hear what was said, but I knew it was no place for me. I walked away.

Somehow I knew Katie wouldn't blame me for not delivering the letter. Bridie would be happy to know it was not too late after all. □

Someone's
Dream

Else's

by
**MARY
SHEPHERD**

IT was a September evening. The sun, just beginning to give up after a long day's vigil, was filling the horizon with soft, gentle shades of gold and purple, and a sighing breeze moved lazily through the tall trees in the park.

Valerie Baynes leaned on a low stone wall and looked over the tranquil scene before her. The lawns dipped into a shallow valley, rising again beyond the man-made streams. Flowers scented the night air, and the gentle sound of water tumbling over rocks rose from below.

The park was beautiful. Why then was she seeing, not the lovely vista in front of her, but a small irregular-shaped area — an area surrounded by rusting railings and stunted trees struggling to keep alive; an area with turf browned by the combination of many feet, lack of care and sunshine?

The little triangular pond was nearly always thick with mud. In the summer it dried up and they had walked across the slimy bed with containers searching for anything alive they could take to school.

In the winter it overflowed, flooding the banks, so they slipped as they made their way over to the rusting, squeaky swings.

Valerie knew there had been many children playing in the park, but it was Rory Williams she remembered. Rory, climbing the forbidden trees, leaning down, looking at her as he chanted:

Redhead, redhead! Scary, scary redhead!

It was Rory who had pulled her pigtails, but gently, with none of the viciousness some of the other boys showed, when unobserved.

None of the children dared mistreat an animal when Rory was around, and it was always Rory who waded into the muddy pool if a boat was stuck.

Rory's clothes were always clean, what there was of them around the boggled areas of darns and patches — and Rory was clever.

129

VALERIE thought back to the evening when it all happened. She had lost a twenty-pence piece in her desk and lingered after school to find it. Neither the teacher, Miss Atkins, nor Rory noticed her at the back of the classroom.

Rory was just leaving when Miss Atkins called him back.

"Rory! This homework is a disgrace! How many times do I have to tell you? You're one of the brightest boys I ever had, there's a good future in front of you. I hoped you would go far, make the school proud of you — but if you won't help? You must do your homework, Rory."

For a moment, silence was heavy in the classroom, then Rory spoke.

A torrent of words came rushing out. There was a note in his voice — a mingling of despair and anger a boy of ten should never know.

"And where do I do it, miss? How do I do it? We've only one room and the table's always full of the kid's stuff. There's four little 'uns and my dad always has the telly on." The last words were almost a sob.

Miss Atkins stretched out a hand, but let it fall again. "The bedroom?" she asked, but without hope.

"I've to climb over two beds to get to mine, and I share that with our Ronald. So you tell me how to do homework, miss!"

Then he ran from the room without waiting for an answer. Miss Atkins didn't call him back, and Valerie watched in amazement as she rubbed the back of her hand over her eyes.

Teachers don't cry, she thought.

Once back in her own semi-detached home, Valerie looked at her room with new eyes. A desk near the window, bookshelves and even a small music centre.

Over the meal she told her parents about Miss Atkins and Rory.

"I thought Miss Atkins was going to cry, but of course she didn't. She's a teacher. I think Rory did though, but I won't tell the others," she added with sudden wisdom.

After the meal Agnes and Norman Baynes walked into their utility room. It had a large work surface, and there was warmth from the central-heating boiler.

"I could fetch a chair down from a bedroom, and clear a couple of drawers so he could leave his books," Agnes said quietly. "It seems such a shame — so many youngsters don't want to work."

"Mmm." Norman looked thoughtful. "I don't see why it shouldn't be the answer. But we will have to tread carefully — mustn't upset his parents. They will be doing the best they can . . ."

"I'll go round and see Emma Williams tomorrow afternoon. I met her at the clinic once or twice when I was helping out."

Valerie never heard what happened between Rory's mother and her own, but she did know the two women became friends.

That night the bell rang and Rory stood there.

"Mum said you wanted to see me," he said quietly.

It was Norman who took him into the little room and told him he could work there any time between six and eight-thirty. Then he led the starry-eyed lad back into the living-room and gave him lemonade.

S O Valerie's friendship with Rory Williams went on over the years. Rory worked hard, and usually finished the evening sitting in the kitchen drinking cocoa and devouring a slice of Agnes's chocolate cake before he went home.

Then he was in the fifth form and there were studying facilities for him at school. Reluctantly, he cleared out his books, thanked Mr and Mrs Baynes and left.

But Rory and Valerie still attended the school dances together; still escaped for walks on the moors whenever Rory could manage it; still talked of the time when Rory would leave university with an honours degree.

And if Rory spoke about it less over the years, Valerie still clung to the dream.

When she was seventeen, she left her Yorkshire home in Willensy to become a student nurse in an Edinburgh hospital. Rory came to her party the evening before she left, but he and Valerie had little time alone.

They had not seen much of each other over the previous eighteen months. Rory had left school and was working for an insurance company — and Valerie had had to work hard to pass her entrance examinations.

Her heart was heavy as he gave her a quick goodnight kiss.

The next morning her parents took her to the station. They were early and there was still ten minutes to go when Rory joined them.

"I got some time off," he told her. "I had to."

Agnes and Norman said their goodbyes and left them alone, and Rory took Valerie's hands in his.

"There was so much I wanted to say last night, but I didn't know how to. Now . . ."

"Rory, it doesn't matter now you've —"

"No, Valerie. Let me talk, there isn't much time. I have to be fair to you. You know Dad's out of work, and there are three of the kids still at school. I have to help out."

"But your plans. You did so well! What about university?"

"Universities won't go away, and there are older students. Don't worry, Valerie, I won't throw it all away. But I had to tell you, I've so little to offer. It will be a long time before I can plan a future. You're so young and pretty." He reached out and touched her hair, auburn now, framing an oval face with deep grey eyes that looked up at him with her heart shining through.

She took his hand and held it. "Rory, you know I —"

He put a finger on her lips. "No, love, not yet. Wait a while. Write to me and I'll write back."

They had written, but gradually the letters had dwindled. Valerie had not been back to Willensy. Soon after she began nursing, her father had taken early retirement and bought a bungalow on the East

131

Coast. From then on Valerie had spent all her holidays there.

VALERIE felt an arm round her shoulders and her cheek rubbed against the familiar harshness of a tweed jacket.

"Andrew! I didn't hear you. How long have you been there?"

"Long enough. You were miles away. Want to tell me?"

He tucked her hand in his arm and they walked down the path towards the park gates.

"I was thinking about Willensy," she told him, suddenly stopping and looking up at him.

"Andrew, I have a long weekend to come. I want to go home — not to Morecambe, but to Willensy. I have a married friend I can stay with."

Andrew Summers looked down at the girl he loved. "And my answer?" he asked gently.

"Give me a little more time, please."

"Come back to me," he told her as his lips found hers. Valerie's arms were soft round his neck, her lips returned his kiss, but still she was conscious of the doubts in her heart.

Two days later she was hugging her friend, Bette Findley.

"Valerie — it's been far too long! Come on, I've got the old banger outside, the baby's asleep on the back seat."

Valerie looked out eagerly as they went through the familiar roads.

"Simon's eating out tonight, so we'll get Darren to bed and eat round the fire," Bette told her as she lifted her small baby from his safety seat. "I want to hear all about this handsome doctor of yours," she teased.

It was about eight o'clock when Valerie stood up.

"Mind if I stretch my legs for ten minutes? I feel cramped after sitting on the train."

Bette glanced shrewdly at her friend, and nodded.

"Good idea! I've a few jobs to do ready for tomorrow. Don't hurry, love."

The September sun was sinking as Valerie sat moving just a little on the old swings. It was just the same. The swings still squeaked, the trees had not grown and the grass was still hard to find. Nothing had changed.

"Bette told me you had gone for a walk. I thought I would find you here."

"Rory." Valerie was not surprised, she knew he would have heard about her visit. After all, she thought honestly, wasn't that why she had come?

"It's been a long time," he said, and they laughed as the squeak of his swing joined hers. "That's one duet I can do without. Come on, let's sit by the pond . . ."

He took her hand and it was as though she had never been away. The words flowed between them — about the hospital, her parents, anything and everything.

Except Andrew.

Rory had a lot to tell. His father had died and his mother remarried.

"A decent bloke. Good to the kids. There's only one at school now. I don't have to worry any longer. I've got an old banger, and my own room. It's not much, but a start."

"And University?" she asked.

Their eyes met, his dark and questioning, hers wondering, hesitant. He had grown up, her Rory. He was tall, decisive, a man to be proud of.

"I don't know," he answered slowly. "It all depends . . ."

Outside Bette's he took her in his arms. "Meet me tomorrow, we'll spend the day together. We need to, Valerie."

Their kiss was light as the brush of fairy wings. As he said, it had been a long time. But Valerie felt it on her lips long after she had drifted into sleep.

THE next morning Rory headed away out of Willensy.

"Scarborough," he told her, and they both laughed. Light, carefree laughter as though the clocks had been turned back. Scarborough! The magic place of Sunday school outings, where the days had been golden, sun drenched, and school was a long way off.

They had a magical day.

Summer

I THOUGHT I would write about summer,
Now it's such an illusive thing,
It's supposed to bring lovely weather
In the days that follow the spring.

But the years flitting by without it,
Make us think of the days gone by,
When we'd play on the beach blithely happy,
Under a wonderful sky.

Now we think ourselves lucky,
If we get just a couple of days,
When we blossom out like the flowers,
In the warmth of the welcome sun rays.

As the following days change to normal,
Dull and chilly-breezed,
We return to the usual comments,
'Bout the weather making us "cheesed."

Well there's nought we can do about it,
Life must still carry on,
I wonder if they'll know about summers,
After we oldies have gone!
— *Lillias Annie Wann.*

They walked round the Marine Drive and dared the open sea in a motor boat. But when Rory would have gone in a café, Valerie stopped him.

"Let's have fish and chips out of the paper again. Just as we used to . . ."

All too soon, evening was sweeping in from the sea. The littered beach told its own story of a sunny day, now over. Rory and Valerie held hands, but were quiet as they slowly walked back to the car.

On the way home Rory pulled in at a small, but select hotel.

"Dinner, m'lady," he told her.

"Rory, let me —"

"No you don't, this is my day. I've waited a long time to be able to do this, Valerie. The table's already booked."

The meal was delicious, the lights low and the music soft. Rory held her close as they danced, his lips buried in her hair. She felt the warmth and strength of his body, and nestled her face against his shoulder.

The moon and stars lit up the sky as they drove home. When the car stopped, Rory took her in his arms, holding her, his lips searching her face, the hollows of her neck, seeking for an answer.

As they drew apart, their eyes met. Rory outlined her face with a gentle finger, feeling her tears.

"Don't cry, little redhead," he told her softly. "Perhaps we waited too long. Perhaps young love is like the grass in the park — it gets trampled on, neglected."

"What will you do?" she asked.

"University, now I know. But you were always there, I nearly came several times, but I remembered how lovely you were, and your letters had stopped. I hadn't the courage. And you?"

"There's a doctor, Andrew Summers, but, like you I had to know, had to be sure . . . Rory, this isn't goodbye? You will come to my wedding?"

He grinned ruefully. "Try stopping me," he said. "And I will expect you both to come and clap when I get that degree. After all, it was thanks to you I was able to study. I've never forgotten, redhead."

He walked with her up the path. "I'll come round tomorrow to see Bette," he told her. "And I'll see you off at the station on Tuesday. And, Valerie, if ever you need a friend . . ."

She reached up and brushed his cheek with her lips. "I know, Rory. There's something special about old friends. Good luck."

☆   ☆   ☆   ☆

Rory drove slowly home. In his own room he sat, reliving the day, his eyes full of wistful sadness.

There would never be anyone for him but Valerie, he knew that. But Valerie hadn't needed to tell him her heart was elsewhere. Perhaps she hadn't known it herself, but Rory, loving her, holding her, had known.

He would get on with his life. There were many things he wanted to do.

Suddenly, he thought of his old teacher — Miss Atkins. And then, he thought of Valerie's parents and how all of them had helped make his dream of university come true.

Perhaps, in time, he could make someone else's dream come true . . . □

A GIFT FOR CHRISTMAS

NOT many people spend Christmas Eve on the seashore, but maybe they ought to, young Stephen thought. It was cold this afternoon, bitterly cold. The wind came whistling across the North Sea, lashing the white horses until they came thundering over the sand.

Most of them were exhausted before they reached the

by
BETTY
McINNES

toes of his school shoes, but some surged in until he was forced to nip smartly out of their way. Already there was a white, salty line along the leather uppers that would annoy his mum.

Shoes cost the earth, he knew — because he'd heard her complain about them often.

Usually Stephen treated his shoes with respect. They'd belonged to his big brother, Allan, first and would be handed down to his little brother, Craig, if there was any mileage left once Stephen had outgrown them.

It was quite a responsibility wearing shoes in trust for Craig, and Stephen tried hard not to scuff the leather too much. When he remembered, that is.

But the state of his shoes was the last thing he worried about this Christmas Eve. He had other, more important things on his mind.

He half-closed his eyes against the wind that bit into his skin and made his cheekbones ache. As usual, he'd scorned to wear the gloves his mother knitted for him, and his fingers were like fat, red sausages as he stooped to comb the tangles of seaweed to see if they hid what he was looking for.

Stephen paused a minute to blow on his painful hands, cupping them round the heat of his warm breath as he gazed at the vastness of sea and sky, so empty.

In the town, just twenty minutes away by bus, the pavement would be thronged, the shops frantic, people everywhere jostling and pushing against one another in a last-minute, frenzied rush.

Here, there was only Stephen. But it wasn't lonely, though. The white horses began their gallop far out in the restless sea and came in tossing their white manes, bucking and plunging, just as Grandad told him.

Stephen stared upwards, open-mouthed at the scurrying clouds, checked in his beachcombing by the sheer majesty of it all. Around him, the white gulls balanced on the wind, laughing and screaming, as jubilant and noisy in their own way as the Christmas crowds Stephen had left behind.

No, it certainly wasn't lonely, he thought, with the frothing waves crashing on the black rocks like the rumble of chariots!

He went back to his engrossing task, poking around in the freezing seaweed with icy fingertips. Most of the shells he found were the ordinary, slate-blue mussel shells with pure, mother-of-pearl linings. Hard, tough shells that withstood the battering of the seas without breaking and crumbling.

The other ones, the rarer ones, the *special* ones, came from a deeper sea. When they had given up the little sea-creature that inhabited them, they were empty and aimless, driven and crumbled by the force of the waves to have their fragile structures broken on the rocks.

Like Grandad, he thought.

Stephen had one such special shell in his hand, still beautiful and complicated and with hidden depths, but old and worn, broken and fragile as white eggshell. Stephen held it tenderly.

He didn't want to add even a fingertip pressure to its buffetting, because it had endured enough. Like Grandad, who was a very special man. It took a special man to be a lighthouse keeper, Mum said.

STEPHEN laid the broken shell on a bed of fresh seaweed, protected. He squinted against the icy wind that made his sight blur with tears and gave the lighthouse on the point a wavy outline. It looked sturdy and strong, outstanding, alone, but not lonely.

When darkness came, it would be brighter than a star in the night of Christmas Day, and on and on, every night until Stephen himself was an old man. Unbelievable! The stretching of time took his breath away, his own twelve years seemed like a minute

Grandad had been a keeper on that rock far out to sea, difficult to pick out now, even with Stephen's sharp eyes. Sometimes, long ago, if a storm raged at Christmastime, the lighthouse ships couldn't make the relief, and then there would be no special Christmas dinner, no Christmas presents even for the keepers on the rock.

You would have to be a very special person to survive that, Stephen thought! He would cry. He would cry his heart out, if there wasn't any Christmas.

Yet Grandad said those were often the best times. The three men sang carols, and if they couldn't sing for toffee, then so much the better! Grandad would sometimes make his famous scones that were as light as feathers, and they would eat them dripping with salty butter and syrup.

Christmas was in the heart, Grandad said. In the heart.

It was different now, though. There were helicopter pads on the remotest rocks and automatic lights that needed no men to watch the mechanism throughout the long nights.

There were televisions and fridge-freezers at the lighthouse stations, and perhaps microwave ovens, too, for all Grandad knew! The need for very special men was not so great, they were few and scarce now — rare, like Stephen's shattered sea-shells.

He picked up another, pouncing on it hopefully, to discover it was just another twisted skeleton, broken by the sea. Grandad said the sea was terrible and powerful, but even a wee laddie could master its power and use it with respect, if he used his brains.

Stephen used his brains, frowning in deep concentration at the tossing crests of the white horses. He saw how recklessly they dashed against the rocks before pounding up the beach to retreat again, leaving behind a trail of torn seaweed and broken shell.

It wasn't the water that broke them, he realised, it was the hard rocks they met on their way, and over there, in the sheltered curve of the bay where there were no rocks, the sea's gallop became a more gentle canter. Suddenly, it came to him, he was looking in the wrong place!

WITH a whoop, Stephen went dashing through the runnels of sea water and the crisp crusts of frozen sand, forgetting about shoes and jeans in trust for his little brother.

He was wet up to the knees when he reached the bay, but here the sand rippled like carved wavelets under his feet and masses of seaweed squelched and made him skid unsteadily when he stood on it. There were more shells than ever here.

He picked up some tiny ones because they were so beautiful, but all the time he was searching, so engrossed he almost forgot to breathe. When he found it, the rare and special one, he could hardly bear to pick it up, in case it was less than perfect.

He took it to the sea and washed it in the waves before examining its curves and folds, pink and creamy, the dark recesses of its secret centre. Perfect!

Stephen removed the blob of bubble-gum from his hankie and wrapped up the shell carefully before putting it in the pocket of his anorak. It was only then that he looked up at the changing sky and saw how dark it had become.

The short afternoon of Christmas Eve was drawing to a close and his mother would be heading home — tired, cross, and expecting to find him there with the other two. Stephen belted up the beach in a panic, sand clinging stiffly to his soaking jeans.

He kept one hand securely on the pocket full of shells as he searched in the other for the bus fare, reassuring himself that the coins were still there.

It felt funny, sitting in the bus returning to the Christmas scene everyone else accepted as normal. Stephen sat looking out and swinging his legs in the vain hope that the movement and heat of the bus would dry his jeans before his mum saw them.

So many people, jostling and pushing, lights everywhere, shop windows brilliant. They'd all be out tomorrow, though, and the people gone. I'd rather have the moving sea and sky, thought Stephen, and the lighthouse lights.

His mum was waiting for him, when he clattered up the tenement stair, and she was tired and cross. She was heartily sick of queuing and shoving and pushing her way around the shops. She just wished the whole season of Christmas could be over.

It wasn't easy being a single-parent, but by scrimping and saving she'd bought expensive toys for her boys and she was confident they'd be delighted. That's what gave her pleasure, that's what Christmas was for, to give the children a good time.

Even Stephen would be pleased, and he wasn't like the other two. He was always coming away with old-fashioned remarks and shooting off on unexpected ploys.

Away to the beach on Christmas Eve! Did you ever hear the like, she thought indignantly. She examined her son, who'd caused her fifteen minutes intense anxiety, and her fears for his safety exploded in irritation.

"Stephen! Will you just look at the mess you're in!"

Higgledy-Piggledy House

THERE'S a higgledy-piggledy house that I know, where the
    windows reflect in a grin,
Where the gate hangs askew and the door opens wide, as if to
    welcome you in.
There are flowers in a riot around a small lawn, though the
    greenery in patches lies bare,
There's a quaintness and charm that seems to prevail
    everywhere.
It's the higgledy-piggledy house of my dreams, where the
    children are growing like flowers,
Despair of the neighbours — delight of my heart and guardian
    of life's golden hours:
Dear higgledy-piggledy house of my dreams, may your bright
    happy memory survive,
Till the days I am old, then though I may be alone, my day-
    dreams will keep me alive.

                           — Georgina Hall.

She could have shaken him in her relief and exasperation.

Stephen looked down at the ruin of his shoes and the caked, wet sand on his jeans and hung his head.

"Awful sorry, Mum."

His brothers were standing behind her, immaculate, not a hair out of place, gloves on. Allan curled his lip with twelve-year-old superiority.

"You dope!"

Craig, the smallest, eyed the ruined shoes with mixed feelings. Perhaps this meant he'd have a new pair of his very own, for once!

Their mother let out a long, persecuted sigh.

"There's no time to change you, Stephen, so you'll just have to go the way you are, and it serves you right!" she told her son severely.

She grabbed three gaily-wrapped parcels and gave one to each boy, then picked up a bunch of flowers with a big, red, Christmas ribbon on it, and ushered her brood out of the flat.

ONCE more on the bus and heading in a different direction this time, Stephen wriggled in discomfort. His feet were chilly in the damp shoes and wet socks, his legs felt sticky and prickly with dried salty water.

He didn't dare complain, though, when his mum was in this mood. He thought about Grandad in his hospital bed, and made himself endure it all stoically.

The hospital, when they reached it, was stiflingly hot, so hot Stephen could hardly breathe. His thoughts turned longingly to the icy cold of the seashore, the wind howling in from Norway.

Clutching their parcels, the boys followed their mother along white corridors which somebody had bravely attempted to decorate with strings of tinsel. Although the hospital was so warm, there was no smell of Christmas about it, Stephen decided, no untidiness and happy confusion of wrapping paper and secrecy and mysterious parcels.

Grandad was in a ward with pale green walls and a wooden floor so highly polished Stephen's damp shoes squeaked when he walked on it. The old man lay absolutely still and quiet in a bed with sheets and pillowcases whiter than any Stephen had ever seen, and a green cover that matched the walls.

There were no wrinkles on the bed linen or the coverlet, only on Grandad's peaceful face. Stephen's mum bent and kissed the old man's cheek.

"Merry Christmas, Dad! We brought you some things. Some Christmas cheer," she said in a chirpy voice.

She put the flowers carefully on the locker, where he could see them, then turned to the boys and motioned towards the bed with her head.

With his brothers, Stephen presented their grandfather with the scarf the old man had no need for, in this heat, the socks he would never wear, and the chocolates he couldn't eat. He accepted the gifts, resting his thin, white fingers briefly on each parcel.

Stephen stood close by, watching for the special smile he'd loved ever since he was a tiny boy. It wasn't there. His grandfather lay in the tidy bed, as pale and brittle as the broken shells on the beach.

There was a painful knot of tears constricting Stephen's chest as he reached into his pocket and pulled out the shell — the special one. The hankie it was wrapped in came out of his pocket with a shower of sand which landed like dust over the coverlet and trickled everywhere.

His mother let out a horrified squeal of outrage.

"Stephen! What d'you think you're doing?"

The shiny quartz in the sand sparkled under the ward lights, and Grandad put out a fingertip in wonder and touched the grains of sand that had appeared miraculously.

Stephen took the shell from the hankie and put it into his grandfather's hand. He watched the thin, blue-veined, old fingers close over it, touching, feeling, exploring, recognising the exquisite shape, scenting the smell of sea and outdoors that rose from its secret centre, into his nostrils.

Stephen leaned close. His mother was twittering and chattering her dismay, but he had forgotten about her. He'd forgotten about everything, except his special Grandad, and the special shell.

"Remember you told me about the white horses, Grandad? How they came galloping in with the wind in their tails?" he whispered.

There was a dawning smile on the old man's pale lips.

"I remember, son."

"I brought them to you, for Christmas. I brought you the sea. It's in the shell. You told me so, Grandad. Remember?"

He was so afraid he wouldn't, that he mightn't care any more about the world outside this stifling hot room where the wind never reached, but he needn't have worried.

Slowly, like a rainbow forming in the sky, the special smile formed on Grandad's lips as Stephen watched and drew in his breath in delight. A light appeared in the old man's eyes, a vigorous light that seemed to Stephen brighter than the brightest stars.

It warmed the little boy in a different way than the oppressive heat of the ward, reaching inside to the beating of his generous, little heart.

"Merry Christmas, Grandad," Stephen said softly.

"Merry Christmas, Stephen," Grandad replied quite strongly, the smile breaking into a chuckle.

He raised the beautiful shell to his ear and held it there, the wonderful, special smile still in place.

Watching him, Stephen could hear the sea, too, and the whistle of the wind in the seagrass, and he wasn't sad any more for Grandad.

They stood around him for a long time in silence, watching, but he didn't speak any more, and presently they all tiptoed quietly away, leaving Grandad with the white horses and the refreshing wind, and the ageless sea. □

by SANDY REID

"A T last." Jan gasped as she gazed at the low building, nestling in the distance. "There it is."

"Where?" Betty puffed for breath.

"Down there," Jan said. "Through the trees at the bottom of the hill."

"Boy, am I glad to see it!" Betty was clearly relieved. "My feet are killing me."

"Mine, too." Jan nodded. "I can't wait to get these boots off and steep my poor feet in a basin of lovely cold water."

"Well, another ten minutes down this mountain-side and we're there. Thank goodness!" Betty sighed. "You and your walking holiday! You said it would be a piece of cake. No bother at all. We would eat it."

"Oh, come on!" Jan laughed. "We've only done about ten miles today and you've got to admit that the view from the top of that mountain was marvellous, wasn't it? Worth every yard of the distance we've walked. And think of the great pleasure it will be to get our feet into a basin of cold water."

"You concentrate your thoughts on your feet," Betty said. "Personally, I'm thinking of my stomach. I hope there'll be a really good dinner tonight."

"Bound to be," Jan said. "Anyway, we'll soon find out. There's the gate of the hostel in front of us."

WALKING INTO

HAPPINESS

143

Half an hour later, their feet safely taken care of and their socks changed, they went through to the little bar.

They were just about to focus their eyes on the dinner menu when two young men burst in. With one voice they called out for two pints, then they spotted the girls.

"Hello," called out one of them — a tall, well-built young man. "Would you care to join us?"

"No, thanks," the girls said. "We've just beaten you to it, but don't let us stop you."

"We won't," the well-built young man said. "Cheers!" he cried, raising his glass. "By the way," he added, "my name's Ian. My friend is Ron. We're on a cycling holiday."

"Lucky you," Jan said. "You've got bikes. We're just walking."

"Walking?" Ian exclaimed. "Where have you come from?"

"Fort William," Jan said.

Ian smiled. "That's a fair distance. But I don't remember seeing you on the road."

"You didn't," Jan said. "But do you remember seeing a blooming great mountain on your right-hand side? You did? Well, we came over the top of that."

"Congratulations!" Ian said. "You have a big heart."

"We also have very sore feet, don't we, Jan?" Betty put in. "Mine are still aching and it's all *her* fault. She talked me into this."

Jan made a quick grimace at Ian. "I confess I'm to blame," she said. "It just seemed a good idea when we planned it."

"You said it would be a great adventure," Betty said. "All kinds of interesting things would happen, you said."

"Just a minute," Ian said. "Your holiday isn't finished yet. I said the same thing to Ron, when we decided to have a cycling holiday."

THEY chatted for a while longer and then all agreed to have dinner together. They had a good laugh at all their misadventures while they ate.

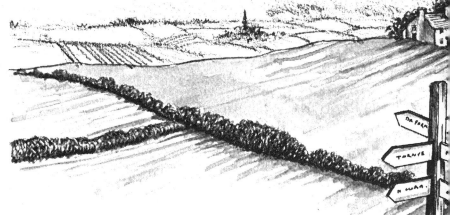

The sun was slowly dipping behind the mountains when they left the dining-room.

"What a beautiful evening," Jan said.

"Anybody feel like a stroll," Ian suggested.

"Oh, not me!" pleaded Betty. "I couldn't walk a yard more today."

"I've had enough for the day, too," Ron put in, "so you can count me out."

Jan smiled at Ian. "All right then, but just for ten minutes," she said. "My feet wouldn't carry me much further."

"Right," Ian said. "I'm not going far either but it is a gorgeous evening."

He turned to Jan. "How about the end of the lane and back?"

As they walked down the lane Ian turned to her.

"When you're not climbing mountains what do you do for a living?"

"I work in a bank in Glasgow," Jan said. "And you?"

"I teach," Ian said, and told her the name of the school in Glasgow where he taught English.

"You're kidding!" Jan said in amazement. "That's my old school. I was there . . . well, it seems a hundred years ago."

"Whereabouts is your bank?" Ian asked.

Jan told him and this time it was his turn to be surprised.

"Well, what do you know! My digs are only five minutes away from there. It's time I started an account with you."

They'd reached the end of the lane when Jan said:

"I'm afraid my feet have had enough and Betty will be waiting for me to get to bed."

"OK," Ian said. "Now where are you heading for tomorrow."

K

"We'll see what the weather's like, but I think we'll make it a short walk," Jan said. "The first wee hotel we come to. There's one about five miles down the road and we'll rest up there."

Ian smiled. "Well, we'll see you at breakfast, I hope."

WHEN they awoke in the morning, the rain was teeming down and the hills were shrouded in mist. All agreed it was no morning for cycling or walking so they decided to have a quiet day and stay where they were.

However, by noon the rain had stopped. Then the mist cleared from the top of the mountains and the sun was beginning to peek through the clouds. By mutual agreement they all decided to set out on their travels.

Before they left Ian managed to sneak a few words with Jan.

"It's been nice meeting you," he said. "I hope we meet up with you again somewhere along the road."

"I've enjoyed meeting you," Jan said. "But there's not much chance of bumping into each other."

"Why not?" Ian asked.

"Well, you travel a lot faster than we do!" Jan laughed. "After all, you're on bikes and we have mountains to climb. However, maybe we'll meet some place on the way back."

"That's a pleasant thought," Ian said. And they all shook hands and set off on their various ways.

"We were going to head for that wee hotel about five miles down the road," Jan said to Betty once the boys had gone. "If we climb that hill to the right and come down the other side we should be just about above it. It shouldn't take more than a couple of hours and we could rest up there for the rest of the day."

"That sounds terrific to me," Betty said. "My feet are still giving me gyp."

"We'll take it easy," Jan soothed, "and we can sit down and have a break when we get to the top of the hill."

☆　　　☆　　　☆　　　☆

Ian and Ron set off at a good pace. The road was smooth and they were both fit young men. After a couple of miles Ian turned to his friend.

"This road is pretty monotonous," he said. "How about cutting down that lane to the right for a bit and wending our way back to the main road later."

"OK," Ron said, "you're the boss. You know where you're going."

So they set off down the lane and at the end of it came to a crossroads.

"Where are we?" Ron asked.

"Your guess is as good as mine," Ian said. "How about taking the middle one of the three."

"Sounds all right to me," Ron said.

The Girls Next Door

JENNIFER and Janet Brown
Live next door to me,
They're twins, but not a bit alike,
As you will plainly see.

Both of them are fun to know,
They call me "Handsome Harry,"
I love them both, but can't decide
Which one of them to marry.

Jennifer has silken curls,
And great big shiny eyes,
But Janet, who's the homely sort,
Makes gorgeous cakes and pies.

Jennifer can sing and dance
Like any TV star,
But people queue for Janet's fudge
At every church bazaar.

This summer, Jennifer was crowned
Upon our village green,
And everybody said she was
The prettiest-ever queen.

But Janet, in her faded jeans,
(The sort of clothes I like),
Will help a fellow bath his dog,
Or mend a punctured bike.

Sometimes I lie awake at night,
Trying to decide
Which of these two lovely girls
I'll ask to be my bride.

If only two could count as one,
My problems would be over,
I'd marry both, and we'd all live
Like honey-bees in clover!

The twins are twenty-one years old,
I'm very nearly ten,
Perhaps I'll wait till I grow up,
And choose my sweetheart then . . .
— *Kathleen O'Farrell.*

Walking Into Happiness

Within half an hour of steep pedalling upwards the sun suddenly disappeared, the clouds closed in and the rain started to fall.

They stopped to put on their rain capes but within a few minutes the rain was dripping down their noses.

"Any idea where we are?" Ron asked.

"None whatsoever," Ian said, "but I think it's a good time to turn back and make for the main road. We'll see what the weather's like down there."

MEANWHILE Jan and Betty had reached the top of the hill when the rain suddenly hit them, so they dived into a fir tree copse for shelter.

Fifteen minutes later Betty shivered.

"This rain is never going to go off. How far away is that hotel we're supposed to be making for?"

"Another half an hour down the hill and along the road should see us there."

"The quicker the better!" Betty replied.

The rain got heavier and heavier as the girls slipped and stumbled down the greasy hillside. Finally, in the middle of the afternoon, soaked to the skin, they stumbled into the little wayside hotel.

The woman behind the tiny reception desk smiled at them.

"Yes, we do have a twin-bedded room with a bathroom adjoining."

Gratefully the two girls stumbled slowly and wearily upstairs.

An hour later, bathed, refreshed and with dry clothing from their rucksacks, they made their way downstairs to the small entrance hall and sat down to tuck into a pot of hot tea and home-made buttered scones.

"You can't beat a walking holiday." Jan laughed.

"You must be joking," said Betty. "But I'll admit these scones are marvellous."

"I wonder how the boys are doing?" Jan asked. "I don't fancy cycling in this kind of weather."

And no sooner had she spoken than the door opened and two soaken and bedraggled young men made their appearance.

"Heavens above!" Jan gasped, jumping to her feet. "Did you fall into the river?"

Ian smiled a very wet smile.

"I agree it's a little damp out there. How did you get on?"

"It was just a bit too damp for us as well," Jan replied. "But we made it. Would you like to join us for tea and scones?"

"We'd love to," Ian said, "but first things first. A bath and a change of clothing seem indicated then you can talk me into a cup of tea."

"And a scone, too," Ron put in.

Twenty minutes later they were back, dried out and looking remarkably spruce and neat.

"Now," Ian said, "get cracking with that tea."

"I didn't expect to see you two so soon," Jan mused. "I thought you had a long trip in mind today."

"We did have," Ron broke in. "But this character got us lost. He took the wrong road. He's supposed to know this country like the back of his hand and instead of staying on the main road we took a turn into the hills.

"We cycled over mountains and got soaked to the skin as well. Then we had to turn back and eventually we made it here."

"Well," Ian said cheerfully. "It all worked out for the best. Here we are all together again and as warm as toast. A perfect ending to not a very successful day!"

Jan smiled happily.

"It could have been worse," she said. "You might have actually finished in the river.

☆   ☆   ☆   ☆

That night after dinner the rain had gone off and the sun had made a tentative appearance.

"Anybody for a stroll?" Ian asked.

"Not me," Betty said.

"I'm game," Jan said.

Ron shook his head. "Count me out. I'll keep Betty company in the bar, if she has no objections."

"Come on then," Ian said. "To the end of the village and back."

Walking Into Happiness

As they strolled down the village street Jan said, "What a pity you got lost and took the wrong turning."

"Who got lost!" Ian said, laughing.

"Well, Ron said you did."

"I had to fool him," Ian explained. "I wasn't very sure if Ron would have agreed with me to try and catch up with you again. So I . . . er, took the wrong turning."

"Why did you do that?" Jan said.

Ian grinned. "I didn't get your telephone number yesterday. That's why."

"And are you going to phone me when we get back to Glasgow?" Jan asked demurely.

"You bet your boots I am," Ian said. "Why do you think I got soaked today?"

"Now I hoped that would be the reason," Jan replied, unable to keep the laughter out of her voice. □

PARTNERQUOTES

TONY CURTIS

1973: *"Acting isn't work — it's a pleasure."*
1982: *"Women have been the root of the great pleasures and pains of my life."*
1985: *"Love is something you have to be really careful about."*

JANET LEIGH

1970: *"With Tony . . . we lasted ten years together, and that's quite a time, in this business."*
1970: *"I've never underestimated love. It's a very powerful emotion."*
Timeless: *"Love at different ages means different things . . ."*

TONY CURTIS & JANET LEIGH — YOUNG HOLLYWOOD LOVE

by CHRISTINE MAXWELL

THE railway station at Fort William is a busy place on summer mornings when the steam train to Mallaig is running. Eager travellers can be seen gathering for the journey, and if there should be a cloudless sky it means that there will be wonderful views of the lovely scenery.

Frequently the train will be fully booked. Travellers seem to feel there is nothing quite like the sound of a massive steam engine puffing its way up a slope, or its distinctive whistle. Even the sight of a trail of smoke drifting past carriage windows can awake nostalgic memories of the time when these things were everyday matters.

Yet it isn't only older folk who want to travel on the train. People of all ages come along, and on Saturdays or when the school holidays are on there are sure to be lots of children . . .

There is Jamie Erskine, for example.

Jamie was nine when he first learnt about the steam train to Mallaig from a television programme. He watched and listened intently, making up his mind to go on it one day.

A steam train you could travel on for nearly two hours! And with a second journey back to where it had started. Wonderful!

As the programme was shown during the winter he realised he would have to wait for the experience. Carefully, he noted down the date in late spring when it would be starting, and then an idea came

150

Steam Train To Mallaig

to him. Yes, why not go on his birthday? Why ever not?

It could be his treat for this year, and when he told his parents he assured them he wouldn't want any other present, just this trip.

His father had agreed to take him, and nearer the time the tickets had been booked and plans made. It was decided to make it a day outing, taking first of all an ordinary train from Glasgow to Fort William. That meant leaving Glasgow at 5.40 a.m.

Why, to be starting out so early would be an adventure in itself.

At last it was the evening before the great event and Jamie was in high spirits. He'd waited for this treat so long . . . Then all at once all the carefully-made plans fell in ruins.

It was as he sat with his parents at their evening meal that his father explained. An important bit of business had cropped up unexpectedly and it must be dealt with next morning — even though it was a Saturday. As head of his firm, John Erskine felt he must do it himself. Perhaps — he looked doubtfully at his wife — perhaps she would go with the boy?

Jamie listened, with sinking heart, to his mother's reply.

"What? Travel away up there at crack of dawn just to go on a smoky old train? I wouldn't dream of doing such a thing!" she exclaimed. "There'll be other days —"

"But you promised I would go on my birthday," Jamie broke in. "You promised ages ago."

His father looked worried.

"You might take him, Louise," he told his wife. "We did promise."

Louise Erskine was tall and slim, and always beautifully dressed, looking hardly old enough to be the mother of a nine-year-old boy. But at that moment her eyes were cold.

"Sorry, no go!" she retorted. "Now, Jamie, you can ring up some of your friends and ask them. to tea tomorrow instead —"

"I don't want friends to tea," cried Jamie. "I want to go on the steam train more than anything else in the world."

He burst into tears.

"If only we knew someone else who was going on that trip tomorrow," his father began.

"Well, we don't," his mother snapped.

So that was that.

JAMIE took refuge in his bedroom once the meal was over. From there he could hear his parents having one of their quarrels. He put his hands over his ears, trying not to listen.

He loved both his parents. When his mother was nice to him she was charming. His dad was super, except when he put business matters first.

Now they had both let him down. And hadn't someone at school said that when your mum and dad quarrelled the next thing was that they parted? Then you stayed with one of them, but not both. Jamie hated the thought of that.

Oh dear, he had never felt so unhappy before. Being let down was awful. It had meant so much to have his treat on the day when he would reach the important age of ten. Now there seemed no hope of it.

Or was there just a faint hope?

He began to recall something that had happened at school just when he was leaving. A relief teacher had been on duty all day, taking the place of his usual one who was off ill. This Miss Reid had been quite nice, and somehow she had discovered that it was his birthday next day.

"Are you having a party?" she had asked kindly as she and Jamie left the classroom together.

"No, I'm going on the steam train from Fort William to Mallaig," he had answered eagerly. "My dad is taking me and we're getting up very early to catch a train at Queen Street Station."

"Really!" Miss Reid had exclaimed. "So am I!"

Jamie had stared in surprise, and as they walked together along the corridor he heard why she was going. It was to get details of the journey for an elderly lady she knew, who wrote travel articles for a magazine and wanted up-to-date information about this journey.

Highland Dawn

THE dreaming loch is
    mirror-still,
Black shadows patch the ben
Where sombre forests climb the hill
Above the sleeping glen.

And then, a single bird's note trills,
Across the listening air.
The veils of mist peel off the hills.
The crags loom stark and bare.

The stars are snuffed out, one by one,
The sky is green and cold,
Until the Midas-touch of dawn
Turns all the hills to gold.

Then rosy beams caress the stream
Creating the most beautiful sight,
And dew-drops in the heather gleam,
Like scattered diamonds bright.

The singing skylark soars aloft
Above the sun-washed brae —
A curl of smoke from waking croft
Welcomes another day.
                    — Brenda G. MacRow.

"But she can't manage to go herself, so she asked me." Miss Reid smiled. "No doubt we'll meet on the train."

"Oh, yes," Jamie had agreed as he left her.

Now he realised there *would* be someone on the train that he knew. Was there any use telling his parents? He didn't think so, for they would want to phone the teacher and talk about it, and of course he hadn't a clue where she lived.

153

But why shouldn't he go off on his own? If any crisis arose he was sure Miss Reid would help him, and if nothing unfortunate happened then he would manage quite well by himself.

The more he thought about it the more he liked the idea.

First of all, he must find the tickets that had been paid for at the time of the booking. Jamie had seen his father throw them into the waste-paper basket, so now he crept down to the dining-room and picked them out of the basket.

Next, he set his little alarm clock for the next morning. It might take twenty minutes to walk to the station, so that should give him plenty of time. He knew he was going to do a pretty awful thing, but a spirit of rebellion had taken over and he was going to do it!

NO-ONE heard him next morning as he got up and dressed after silencing the clock. He took all the money there was in his piggy bank, as well as the ten-pound note Grandpa Erskine had kindly sent for his birthday.

He went over it in his mind. Glasgow to Fort William first. Yes, he had enough to pay for that journey. Then the steam train to Mallaig. He had the tickets for that in his pocket so there would be something left for food during the long day.

How cold and quiet it seemed as he let himself out of the house. He'd never been out at this hour before, and didn't like it much. Few people were about, and no-one took any notice of him as he hurried along, glad when he got to the station.

Now he decided it might be a good idea to avoid Miss Reid at present. No-one could ever tell what a grown-up might do. Supposing she sent him home at once? No, he wouldn't risk a meeting, not until he was safely on to the steam train.

There she was! Jamie dodged behind a stout man who was studying the indicator board, then noted which part on the train she got into, finding a seat for himself as far away as possible.

The train started. That was the first hurdle over, and he could relax and look out at interesting things through the window. Nobody took much notice of him, just a woman who offered him some sweets, and a man who asked him the time as his own watch had run down.

It was a lovely journey and Jamie enjoyed every minute of it, looking with awe at the big mountains which came into view, and marvelling at the wild swampy ground they passed over on Rannoch Moor. It was shortly before ten that the train reached Fort William, and once again he resolved to keep out of Miss Reid's way until the next train had started.

Once on it, he simply couldn't be sent home until he had completed the journey!

Keeping a wary eye on the teacher, he made his way to the ticket office and explained that one of his tickets wouldn't be used. The man he spoke to seemed pleased.

"Thanks, sonny," he said. "The train's fully booked today and someone has just been after a ticket." He called across the counter to a young man who was turning over some leaflets.

"You're in luck," he told the man. "There's a place for you after all."

Jamie got on the train just as it was about to start. There was the whistle, and there was the guard waving a green flag. The train began to move. Good! He was safe.

Happily he moved to the carriage where his seat was — rather taken aback to find Miss Reid actually in the seat opposite his own one. But it didn't matter now if she recognised him.

Jamie's seat was at the window, facing the engine. He squeezed past the young man who had been at the ticket office, and who now occupied the place where his father would have been. Settling himself

▶ *over*

PARTNERQUOTES

PAUL NEWMAN
1988: *"Joanne is endlessly fascinating to me and always will be."*

Eternal, about keeping his head amidst adulation of women: *"Why go out for a hamburger when you have steak at home . . ."*

JOANNE WOODWARD
1968: *"I married late because I remembered what my great-grand-mother told me about getting married: 'Could you see yourself talking to him over breakfast for fifty years?' I can with Paul."*

PAUL NEWMAN & JOANNE WOODWARD — A LOVE THAT STAYED

comfortably, he opened the folder which he had brought, with a good map, and interesting notes about the route.

There was the first place of interest — Banavie, with the series of locks on the Caledonian Canal, known as Neptune's Staircase. And that must be Ben Nevis!

This was really exciting, Jamie thought, as he gazed at the mountain, and thought how it was the highest in the British Isles. And today it was clear at the top, none of the cloud there which his folder told him often obscured it.

What came next? Oh, a commentary was beginning, describing what they were passing. He must listen . . .

Then he heard his name spoken.

"Hello, Jamie," Miss Reid said. "I thought we would meet."

HE smiled at her, not sure what to say, and bewildered by the words she now spoke to the young man who had got the ticket.

"Your son and I met yesterday at the school," she began.

Help, thought Jamie. She must imagine the man was his dad. Now it would all come out that he was alone. He listened to the reply given by the man beside him.

"Sorry, I don't quite understand," he was saying. "Have we met before?"

"No, but aren't you Jamie's father?" she got out awkwardly.

He grinned. "No, I haven't a family yet, nor a wife either, for that matter!"

Jamie pretended to be very absorbed in the scenery. But here it came — the question he dreaded.

"Jamie!" Miss Reid said. "Your father *is* with you, isn't he?"

There was nothing for it but to tell the truth.

"He couldn't come," Jamie mumbled. "Mummy didn't want to, so I just got up early and came by myself."

"But did your parents let you do that?"

"They didn't know. They were asleep when I got up."

He turned again to the window, but heard Miss Reid speak to the man.

"His parents must be worried by now if they don't know where he is. What should we do?"

"Put through a phone call from Mallaig?"

Jamie breathed a sigh of relief. He liked that young man who was sensible enough not to have wild ideas of getting the train stopped and sending him home. Then he stopped listening as they talked on.

Grown-ups had such strange ideas, he mused. These two seemed to think it remarkable that they both lived in Glasgow — as if millions didn't live there!

Presently, he heard Miss Reid say she simply must start writing things down.

"I've missed quite a bit, haven't I?" She laughed. "Never mind, there's always the journey back. Now I wonder what that monument down there is, at this end of a long loch?"

Jamie suddenly took a live interest in the proceedings.

"It's Glenfinnan," he informed her. "It's where Prince Charlie met the Highlanders who were going to fight for him."

"Thanks, Jamie," Isobel Reid said as she wrote busily on her pad.

Quite a lot was written as the train wound on its way, past lochs and hills, over bridges, through tunnels, and with breathtaking views of the sea presently.

Jamie felt blissfully happy as he followed the route on his map and looked out for the small stations they passed. Finally, after a glimpse of the white sands of Morar they arrived at Mallaig where the line came to an end.

There was a chance here to go along the platform and admire the engine. It was a thrill when the kindly driver hoisted him up into the cab and showed him what was done to make the engine go. Slightly grubby, he was put back on the platform and found Miss Reid awaiting him. It seemed she had made the suggested phone call to his home in Glasgow.

"I spoke to your mother," she told him. "No-one had realised you were missing until breakfast time, and no-one dreamed you would have gone on the train by yourself. So both your parents have been terribly worried and they had just asked the police to start looking for you."

Jamie scuffed his shoes on the platform and didn't know where to look. After what happened last evening, he hadn't thought his parents would worry much about where he was. Well, it seemed that they had, so he would be in real trouble when he got home.

He was pretty sure, too, that Daddy and Mummy would be quarrelling worse than ever. Mummy would say it was all Daddy's fault, and he would say it was hers. Well, whatever punishment was in store for him he would just have to take it. In the meantime, he'd try not to think about it.

Fortified by packets of crisps and a carton of juice, Jamie found he was able to enjoy the return journey to Fort William. Once there, he had a farewell look at the engine, then followed Miss Reid out of the station. He was really glad now that she was there, since there were over two hours to wait until the train for Glasgow.

By now he knew that the name of the friendly young man was Mr Henderson. And it seemed that he had a splendid idea.

"I'll be very pleased if you two will come with me and have a meal at a restaurant I know in the main street. What do you say, Jamie?"

"Yes, please!" was Jamie's happy reply.

"It would be most kind of you," Miss Reid said, but she too looked pleased.

By the time the meal was over they were all very good friends. Jamie was glad to know he would sit with them on the long journey back to Glasgow. Somehow he felt that when they arrived there they might protect him if Daddy was furious.

Miss Reid had said that someone was to meet him at Queen Street Station, and he was sure it would be his father.

A S the train crossed Rannoch Moor again, Charles Henderson spoke of the difficulties there had been in constructing that part of the line. He recalled the story of how a party of men had set out one wintry day to walk across and see if they could plan a route.

One man had somehow got cut off from the others and by the next morning they had given him up for lost. It was thought he might have fallen into one of those sinister pools of dark water, or even perished simply from lack of shelter.

But he hadn't. He had strayed a long way from his friends, but managed to find a small cottage which would shelter him for the night. And that was the man who went on to become ultimately Sir Robert McAlpine, one of the great men in the construction world, and whose name can still be seen on notice boards where work is being done by the firm he started.

How awful to be lost in the dark on Rannoch Moor, thought Jamie, as he looked out. But how wonderful that clever men had at last found a way to build this railway line.

It was as the train neared Glasgow that Jamie began to quake inwardly. When it drew to a halt at the platform, he looked out nervously. Then his eyes opened wide. Both his parents were there!

What was more, they came forward holding hands, not at all as if they had been quarrelling fiercely. He was quickly pulled into his mother's arms, then into his father's, and he was hugged in a way that hadn't happened for ages.

He gazed from one to the other in bewilderment.

"Jamie," Louise Erskine said shakily. "I'm sorry. I didn't realise you wanted to go on the train quite so much."

"I'm sorry too, son," his father told him. "I should have gone with you, and after all there was someone else handy to clear up that business. It was dreadful when I heard you were missing . . . I came home at once . . . But why didn't you say you knew someone who would be going on the train?"

"I didn't remember at first," Jamie confessed. "I thought you might not let me go, anyway."

He simply couldn't understand why all at once Daddy and Mummy seemed to be good friends again. He would need to be a good bit older before he realised that a deep anxiety can be a uniting thing.

So it was warm thanks the Erskines gave to the two young people who had looked after their son, and had relieved their anxiety with that phone call.

"It's too late now but we must see you again soon and hear all about your journey together," John Erskine said .

"Come to tea tomorrow," Louise Erskine invited, obviously under the impression that the two were close friends.

It was Isobel Reid who answered first, with a slight blush.

"Thank you. That would be very nice," she replied.

"It would be great!" Charles Henderson said happily. □

by
BEN
MATTHEW

GATEWAY TO HAPPINESS

H ELLO, Becky! You're late coming home. I thought Thursday was your half day." Wilma Johnson smiled as she looked up from sweeping her garden path.

The pretty dark girl to whom she had spoken, stopped and leaned over the low gate.

"It is, but we've been doing the Christmas decorations!"

Wilma looked at the girl's happy face framed in dark curls. "You look as though you've enjoyed it, anyway."

"Oh, I have! I love to see the children's faces when they come into the store. And look what I got for Cindy. The manager gave me it because it was damaged."

Wilma took the small doll and looked down at the painted, china face. One arm was held to the sawdust body by only a thread.

"I know Cindy wants a fairy doll for Christmas, and thought, well I could sort of put some tinsel round it . . ." Becky's voice wavered as though she was suddenly uncertain of her own capabilities.

Wilma intended handing the doll back, but surprised herself by asking Becky if she would like her to dress it.

The girl's face lit up. "Oh would you? I'm not very good at sewing. I'm sure you'll do it much better."

Sometime later, Wilma walked round to the back of the house and put her brush away before going indoors. Hanging her coat in the small porch, she looked down at the doll.

Why had she offered? She didn't really want to get involved — not at her age.

She had been living in her pleasant semi-detached house for eight or nine months. Beech Avenue was a wide, tree-lined, peaceful place, but now Alice's eyes wandered to the little path at the top. The path led to a row of poorer houses, crowded together at either side of the narrow street. Alice hadn't been up the path but she had seen the same thing over and over again in the town.

Becky lived there, and so did Cindy.

Wilma had met Becky a few weeks earlier. The older woman had been quite unaware that a folded ten-pound note had fallen out of her purse as she fumbled for the key before reaching her gate. Becky had knocked at the door, the note in her hand, and, since then, the two often stopped for a chat.

On one occasion Wilma was passing the store where Becky worked just as the young girl was leaving for lunch. Wilma had insisted on taking her to a café where they shared toasted sandwiches.

It was then Becky had told Wilma about Cindy, who lived with her mother and two older brothers, Jack and Rodney, a few doors away from her; told how an accident had committed her to a wheel-chair.

WILMA turned from the window and went upstairs. She came down with a large bag of fabric pieces and tipped them out, forming a splash of colour on the grey carpet.

Thoughtfully she picked up a square of rose pink taffeta, and smiled. She remembered the day when, as head cutter in the gown shop where she had served her apprenticeship, she had told a new junior to lay the pattern pieces on to the length of rich, glowing fabric.

But, the girl, thinking she was using her initiative had cut round them regardless of straight grain, warp or weft.

Wilma had been close to tears. The fabric was ruined and she told the young girl so in no uncertain terms.

Of course, it had all blown over. The firm had ordered more silk and Wilma had cut it out herself. The girl though, did not return, and Wilma always remembered how sorry she was for losing her temper.

The lesson had stood her in good stead and she had stayed with the same firm until retiring. Then, feeling restless and wanting a change, she had moved to this quiet town, where her married sister had lived for some years.

Her sister Megan's lifestyle though, was very different to the one Wilma wanted — bridge, golf . . . Wilma enjoyed none of these things and found time heavy on her hands.

Now, she looked down at the rose-coloured fabric she was holding and, rather reluctantly, decided it was quite wrong for a fairy doll. Wilma laid it on one side and carefully sorted out scraps of white satin, but time and again her eyes strayed to the splash of rose. A fairy prince! Every fairy doll should have a prince. Cindy's would have one, she decided.

The December sun was bright but cold. Wilma shrugged on her warm coat and, after hesitating a moment or two, walked up the avenue to the narrow path. Cindy Grant was there in her chair. The cold had brought colour to her cheeks and tipped her nose with a glow almost as bright as the fabric Alice had been handling.

Cindy was warmly, if clumsily, tucked under a blanket and she flashed Wilma a smile.

Wilma smiled back and walked on. When she came back from the shops, the doll that was destined to be a fairy prince safely in her bag, the little girl was not there.

A day or two later she saw the ambulance pull up. The house door opened and Josie Grant hurried out and lifted her small daughter down. Josie was big, blowsy and untidy, but Wilma saw her cheerful smile and heard the affection in her voice as she spoke.

She also saw Cindy wince as the big woman clutched her tightly to carry her into the house.

The following day as Wilma was returning home she saw Cindy's chair propped near the wall outside a shop. The child looked cold and near to tears.

"Cindy! What's wrong, love?" Wilma asked anxiously.

"It's our Jack! Mam kept him off school to look after me so she could go and do some work. He's left me here while he went with his friends. Said he wouldn't be long but —" The threatened tears trickled slowly down her pinched cheeks.

Wilma smiled. "Never mind! I'll wheel you home and you'll soon be warm."

THE house was empty when they got there. It was untidy but clean. The living-room was liberally festooned with paper streamers, balloons and any trimmings the children had been able to devise.

Cindy looked round, her blue eyes alight. "Isn't it lovely? It's for Father Christmas. He's going to bring me a fairy doll."

Wilma looked down at her. "Cindy, what time will your mother be home?"

"Don't know, but I'll be all right now. Mam will bring some fish and chips in." But the little girl still looked pale and upset.

Wilma suddenly made up her mind. She picked up the child's crayon and drawing book. Quickly she scribbled a note, then smiled at the little girl who was slowly but surely creeping into her heart.

"I'm taking you to my house," she declared. "I've told your mother I'll bring you home at five o'clock."

When they reached Beech Avenue Wilma lifted the small girl and carried her into the house. Cindy looked round at the deep and

L   161 comfortable chairs, pale carpet, the long velvet drapes and Wilma watched her changing expressions with interest.

Then she helped her comfortably on to the settee.

The child looked up, her eyes wide with surprise. "You haven't got any Christmas! I thought everybody had some Christmas!"

Nonplussed, Wilma murmured something about not bothering, being on her own, and perhaps she might, later on. Then she found a glossy magazine for her unexpected guest and went into the kitchen. Quickly she heated blackcurrant juice and set out a plate of biscuits.

Cindy's face lit up as Wilma put a small table beside her and handed her the steaming beaker.

"Drink every drop, then you'll feel nice and warm."

By the time the beaker was empty and Cindy had started on the biscuits she looked her old self. She chatted away about Christmas, her brothers, and told how her mother couldn't go out to work as much now Cindy was in a wheel-chair.

Wilma listened and steered the conversation round to Cindy's hospital visits.

"They rub my legs and put them in some stuff. I have to hold on to some bars and try to walk but it hurts. Mam lets me off at home because it hurts. She says it will come right on its own."

Wilma found the afternoon flying by and soon it was time to tuck Cindy into her chair and wheel her home. Josie Grant, just going in with a huge paper parcel of fish and chips, stared as she saw them. And when Cindy told her what had happened the woman exploded.

"Just you wait till I get hold of our Jack! I'll teach him a thing or two."

Wilma walked thoughtfully home. She had found out who Cindy's home doctor was. A plan was forming in her mind. But dare she?

THE next day she sat facing Dr Waring.

"It's about Cindy Grant. She says she should be doing exercises at home, but her mother lets her off."

"Mmm!" I suspected as much. I have been round to see her as a matter of fact, but she swears Cindy does them, so there's not much we can do. But the child should be making more progress . . .

Then, slowly, Wilma told the old doctor what she had in mind.

He nodded thoughtfully. "A very good plan. If you like I could arrange for you to sit in at the hospital for one of Cindy's treatment sessions. Then you'll see exactly what is needed. I'll fix it as soon after Christmas as I can."

That evening Wilma called Becky Burton in to see the finished dolls.

She was thrilled. "They're beautiful! You must give her them yourself."

Wilma shook her head. "No. I think we'll let Father Christmas take the credit for these. I'm going to ask them all round for tea on Sunday, though. Would you like to come. Sort of help me entertain them?"

Shattered Peace

I WALKED on a green, secluded path,
  Soft overhung by trees,
Beside a gently-trickling stream
  That rippled in the breeze.

A gaily painted barge appeared
  To glide through watery ways,
And families of ducks sailed by
  In feather-fine displays.

Two swans with cygnets floated by
  In silence dignified,
And then a fussy dog chased up
  And barking, stopped his stride.

He ventured to the water's edge,
  At swans to make a pass,
But Father Swan, his white wings
    spread,
  Flapped, hissed and swam to grass.

He made towards the dog in rage
  And cowed, the puppy turned,
With tail between his legs he ran,
  His bright advances spurned.

The swan rejoined his family,
  His feathers like a fleece,
The small birds sang sweet melodies
  And once more all was peace.
              — *Margaret Comer.*

Becky stared. "All of them?" she asked, astonished.

"Yes. A pre-Christmas party. That is if you will come . . ."

The following morning was damp and Cindy was not outside.

Wilma knocked on the door and the little girl greeted her excitedly.

"I've got a present for you. Look! I've been working all the time."

The child held out her thin arms. They held masses of rough, brightly coloured, home-made paper chains.

Josie Grant looked on anxiously. "I told her you wouldn't want them," she said, "but she was determined."

"But I do want them!" Wilma felt a warmth flooding through her. "They're lovely! Actually, I was going to ask if you would all like to come to tea next Sunday? I though it would make a nice change for you all — and for me," she added hastily.

Josic looked surprised, but soon realised her visitor was genuine and, drawing herself up to her not inconsiderable height, accepted the unexpected invitation with dignity.

The next day, Wilma fixed up Cindy's paper chains, added a few balloons and even managed to trim a small Christmas tree. She bought a paper Father Christmas table-cloth and gaily-coloured crackers.

The afternoon was a great success. The children were well behaved, and although they ate with gusto when they sat down at the laden table, a look from their mother was enough to quell any disturbance. Becky had brought some games round and the usually silent house rang with laughter.

Wilma had brought presents for the children, sweaters for the boys and Becky, and a warm track-suit for Cindy. She sensed that Josie Grant would accept for her family, but resent any suggestion of patronage of being given a gift herself.

Sometime during the afternoon, Wilma became Auntie Wilma and, as they were leaving, Cindy put her arms round her and hugged her.

"It's been nearly like Christmas and your streamers look lovely! Can I come again?"

Wilma nodded. "You know you don't need to ask. Look, Jack — you tuck Cindy into her chair and set off for home. Keep an eye on Billy. Your mother won't be a minute, but I want to talk to her."

As the children left, Wilma glanced over at Josie.

"Mrs Grant," she said tentatively, "I wondered if you would let me have Cindy two or three mornings a week. You could do regular work . . ."

Wilma stopped. Instead of looking pleased, Josie Grant's face had closed up, and her eyes were unfathomable as she looked at Wilma.

"Look," she said awkwardly. "I know you mean well — so do all the other do-gooders who keep coming round. But none of you know what it's like to love your kids so much it hurts inside when you can't give them things. Maybe if I was a different mother, more clever, I would be able to help Cindy. Perhaps I'd even be able to get her to walk again. You mean it now, but if you get tired . . . I don't want any of my kids hurt — especially Cindy." She stopped, face flushed, intent.

Wilma looked at the big woman in the overtight dress, the powder inexpertly dabbed on her cheeks, the bleached hair in tight, home-permed curls, and she knew she had been allowed a privileged peep into another's heart. A heart full of love.

"I'll never hurt Cindy, Josie," she said softly. "I promise."

★   ★   ★   ★

The following Wednesday, Josie Grant wheeled Cindy through the narrow path into Beech Avenue.

"Please," Cindy asked. "Can we go to the shops? I want to buy Mam a present."

FOR MORE WONDERFUL READING

Hope you've enjoyed the stories you've read here. If so, you'll be sure to enjoy the heartwarming stories and serials which appear every week in that popular magazine — "The People's Friend."

And there's also cookery, knitting, features and even fun for the kids within its pages.

For information about subscription rates, ask your local newsagent, or write to: Subscribers' Dept., People's Friend, Bank Street, Dundee DD1 9HU.

So they went to the small shopping centre, and, to Cindy's delight, finished off the trip with ice-creams in a warm, brightly-lit café.

Back at Beech Avenue, Cindy looked at the initialled comb case she had chosen for her mother with pride. Then her eyes became wistful.

"I wish I could get her a special present — something really nice."

Wilma smiled. "I think the best present your mother could have would be to see you walking again," she said gently.

Cindy looked at her. "But I can't . . ."

"You might, if you did your exercises properly."

"But Mam hurts me. The nurse hurts a bit, but when Mam does them . . ."

Wilma touched her shoulder. "Can you keep a secret, Cindy?"

The blue eyes sparkled. "Oh, yes! I love secrets."

"Well, I went to see your Dr Waring last week. He says I can go to the hospital and watch how the nurse helps you. Then I thought I could help you when you come to see me. I'll try not to hurt, but your legs aren't going to get well if you won't help them. You do want to be able to walk again, don't you?"

Cindy nodded eagerly. "Yes, but —"

165

"I thought we could plan it, just us two. Then you can really give your mother a special present."

Cindy looked thoughtful for a moment. "Mam has a birthday in three months' time. Do you think —"

"We could try," Wilma said.

She saw the fight going on in the child's mind; saw her eyes go to the thin, scarred legs, and her heart ached for her.

Then she saw the child was watching her, and slowly a look of resolve firmed the childish lips.

"Thank you Auntie Wilma. I'll try not to be a baby. Honest!"

ON Christmas Day, Wilma walked through the path on her way to her sister's home. It was bright and sunny and Cindy was looking out for her.

"Look! Look what Father Christmas brought me. A fairy doll and a fairy prince." Cindy was cradling her treasures in her arms.

As Wilma looked at the child's delighted expression, she knew her work had been worthwhile. Just then, Josie Grant called her in.

"Please, Wilma, I want to say thank you. Becky told me. All that work. Just remember, any time you want any help, well, I'm here for what I'm worth," she finished ruefully.

Wilma looked round the untidy room, saw the fading Christmas tree — put up far too early to even hope to survive Christmas — and listened to the happy laughter from the next room.

"You're worth an awful lot, Josie," she said slowly. "You make your family happy, and they love you."

She took the thick, cheap glass of cheap sherry that Josie held out. "Happy Christmas," she said.

"A Christmas blessing," Josie replied softly, "to each and every one."

Then as Wilma was leaving, Josie slipped a small envelope into her hand. "Not much, but please have it," she whispered.

In the quiet of the park Wilma took out a white lace-trimmed handkerchief. It had obviously lain folded in the paper for a long, long time. How often had Josie Grant, with so few lovely, delicate things in her life, taken it out and looked at it; touched it and put it back.

Wilma's eyes were moist as she slipped the packet back into her pocket.

Soon she would sit at her sister's polished table. The mahogany would reflect the lighted candles. The flowers would be low, perfectly arranged, and they would drink wine out of crystal glasses. There would be expensive presents to hand out.

But as the dead leaves crackled under her feet, as she breathed in the cold, crisp air, Wilma knew that no present would mean more than the lace handkerchief, no wine would taste better than the glass of cheap sherry and no words would be more sincere than a Christmas blessing given by a mother who had so little to give.

"A Christmas blessing," Wilma repeated, "to one and all." □

THE TRUTH WILL OUT...

by Elsie Jackson

D ORIS TAYLOR could hear the voices from the next-door garden clearly as she unpegged her washing. Young Mrs Kerr had invited Mrs McBain, round for afternoon tea before they went along to the school to collect their children.

They were making the most of the June sunshine and their chatter about the children's progress at school and their holiday plans took Doris back thirty-five years to when Tony had been a small schoolboy.

Her eyes grew dreamy as she recalled those idyllically happy days before George had died. For a moment it seemed as though it were only yesterday . . .

Then suddenly Doris stiffened and her cheeks turned pink.

"How are you getting on with Mrs T.?" Mrs McBain was asking in a lower voice, but one that Doris could hear perfectly well.

"Oh dear!" Mrs Kerr groaned. "She doesn't get any better, I'm afraid. She was on the phone again last night complaining about Stewart kicking his football against her fence."

"Who does she think she is?" Mrs McBain demanded indignantly. "People like her should live in the middle of a field where no-one can annoy them. Why she wanted to move into a street like this, I can't think."

"I gather it was because she had no time to pick and choose," Mrs Kerr said dryly. "She had sold her big house in The Avenue and had to find somewhere else quickly."

"So she feels she's come down in the world, does she?" Mrs McBain snorted.

"It's not just that. Women of her age with no children just don't understand how rowdy growing youngsters can be." Mrs Kerr sighed.

Doris didn't wait to hear any more. Lifting her basket of washing, she hurried back into the house. To her annoyance she found she was trembling from head to foot.

How dare those silly young women discuss her behind her back, she thought angrily. How dare they jump to conclusions! Just because she wasn't prepared to sit back and watch her property being destroyed, she was classed as a killjoy, someone who didn't understand children.

But they were quite right about one thing. It *had* been sheer necessity that had brought her here to Redburn Drive. If only she hadn't listened to that stupid financial adviser three years ago who had lost most of her savings for her! If only Sally, her daughter-in-law, had been a different sort of person and had come to her aid!

The "if onlys" were endless. But what was the point, Doris thought with a sudden overwhelming feeling of despair. All that she had once treasured had been taken from her.

First George. Then Tony. Finally her home with all its happy associations. She could see no ray of light in the future. She almost gave in to her grief for a moment.

Then, with a characteristic gesture she straightened her shoulders and marched across the living-room to the corner cupboard. Pulling it open, she took out her weaving frame. There was a piece of half-finished work on it, the second side of one of her "Indian" holdall bags. A neat pile of completed bags lay on the floor of the cupboard.

When she had lived in The Avenue they had sold like hot cakes at the local church's sales of work. But she was too proud to take them back there now. And she hadn't felt like joining the modern little church at the corner of Redburn Drive.

She sat down now and began work on the red-and-brown zigzag section where she had left off.

As she worked, Doris's thoughts reverted to another long-ago June day — when twelve-year-old Tony had come rushing in from school brandishing his "present" for her.

"Here you are, Mum! And I hope you appreciate it," he had said with a cheeky grin. "It's a weaving frame, in case you didn't know. And I spent all this term in woodwork making it."

"Darling! How clever of you!" Doris had cried, not daring to confess that she hadn't the first idea how to use the frame.

Equally impressed, Tony's father had soon remedied that state of affairs by buying Doris several books on the subject.

But when Tony left school, his charm and confident manner had got him a salesman's job in a local gent's outfitters. His flair for the business had earned him speedy promotion. When he was only twenty-five he had opened his own shop in the town.

He had brought Sally home that same year. A pretty, quiet, intelligent girl, she worked in the office of the lawyer that handled Tony's business affairs.

Doris had liked Sally well enough even from the start, but had felt she might be difficult to really get to know. This had proved to be only too true as it turned out.

For after Tony's tragic death in a road accident two years ago, Doris had discovered she really did not know Sally at all. Not until she was in the deepest financial difficulty had Doris written to her daughter-in-law, telling her of her problems.

And all she had received in reply had been a letter of sympathy.

Doris had been unable to hide her bitterness. She had poured out her hurt and anger in a long letter to Sally. She had told her she never wanted to see her, or hear from her again.

In doing this, she also cut herself off from her only grandchild, two-year-old Vicky. Her loss, in this direction, was Sally's fault, too, she felt.

HALF an hour later Doris removed the completed piece of fabric from the frame and placed it with its neighbour ready to machine sew. A familiar thud-thud from the back garden drew her to the window.

Her lips tightened. Young Stewart next door was kicking his football against the wall of his own house, but it wouldn't be long, Doris knew, before it hit the boards of her fence. Sure enough, two minutes later the ball sailed over into her small garden.

She hurried out, picked it up and took it back indoors. Let the boy or his parents come for it if they wanted it back! Then she would give them a piece of her mind.

★   ★   ★   ★

The front doorbell rang at seven o'clock that evening just as Doris had settled down in front of the television with a cup of tea. She sighed with exasperation.

By now she was wishing she hadn't kept Stewart Kerr's football. She had only let herself in for another unpleasant scene, whether it was with the boy himself or with his parents. She collected the ball from the kitchen and walked heavily to the door.

But when Doris finally opened the door, the football dropped from her hands. Her face turned white.

"How did you find me?" she asked the young woman who stood on the step, a small girl clutching her hand.

"Your neighbour in The Avenue gave me your address," Sally Taylor said quietly.

"We got a bus into town. Then we got another bus here," Vicky informed her grandmother, yawning widely.

Doris noticed the large, rather shabby-looking hold-all Sally was carrying. She was obviously expecting to stay for the night at least.

There was no question of turning her away, no matter how she had behaved. After all, Doris thought, little Vicky is my flesh and blood. And she can't help her mother's hard-heartedness.

She smiled for the first time. But only to the child.

"You must be very tired and hungry with all that travelling," she said to Vicky. "It's just as well I've got a spare bedroom. Come in, then."

"It's a lovely house," Vicky said, looking wide eyed round the brightly-painted little hall.

"Not nearly as nice as Granny's last house," Doris said, leading the way into the living-room. "But I don't suppose you remember it."

"It's nicer than our house anyway," Vicky said decisively.

VICKY was an attractive child. She had her mother's dark good looks, but Tony's radiant smile. She chattered non-stop, following Doris around the kitchen as she made eggs and chips for her visitors and whipped up an "instant" dessert.

Soon Doris realised something very important. Despite the ill-feeling between herself and Sally, her daughter-in-law had not turned the child against her. She was grateful for that.

"I've been saving up for ages to come and see you, Gran," Vicky informed her as she stood on tiptoe to look out of the window. "You've got a lovely garden, too. We haven't got a garden."

"Of course you have." Her grandmother smiled, remembering the smart suburban villa her son had bought five years ago. "You're kidding me, Vicky Taylor."

► p172

UNION TERRACE GARDENS, Aberdeen, did not exist 200 years ago. The miniature valley was there, of course, but it was populated by the families of men who worked in ship-building. They lived on the banks of the Denburn, a small river which still exists but whose course has been changed. A railway line has used this valley, and now the banks boast beautiful flower displays. In the background can be seen His Majesty's Theatre, acknowledged by some experts to be the most beautiful in the land.

Incidentally, the shipworkers of the Denburn built the world's fastest clipper — the Thermopylae. The Cutty Sark may be known to most people, but the Thermopylae easily beat Cutty Sark's time from London to Australia.

UNION TERRACE GARDENS, ABERDEEN : J CAMPBELL KERR

"No, Gran. We haven't a garden in our new house," Vicky said earnestly.

"Oh, I see. I didn't know you'd moved," Doris murmured.

She felt uncomfortable, aware of Sally, sitting quiet and polite in the living-room like a stranger. She didn't want her daughter-in-law to think she was quizzing Vicky for information.

"We've moved to a small flat," Sally said shortly when Doris carried the loaded tray through to the living-room. "I have a part-time job in a solicitor's office so it doesn't leave me much time for gardening."

Doris raised her eyebrows, a gesture which she hoped showed Sally just what she thought of her selfishness. Fancy depriving the child of a garden just because she had decided to go out to work!

It wasn't as if she even needed to work! But since she obviously wasn't happy staying at home, surely she could have found a gardener? Too mean, Doris decided, inspecting both mother and child covertly while little Vicky prattled away.

Vicky was wearing last year's summer dress. Doris could see the mark where the hem had been let down. And she was sure she recognised Sally's suit as one she used to wear years ago. Whatever the young woman was doing with Tony's money, she certainly wasn't spending it either on herself or on Vicky!

Tony would have been furious at her, Doris decided, her lips tightening. He had been very conscious of appearances. He had always bought the best and had expected Sally to do likewise.

Doris refused Sally's offer of help with the washing-up. She said the dishes could wait. Then, as soon as Sally took Vicky upstairs to put her to bed, Doris darted into the kitchen.

She had the dishes washed, dried, and stacked away long before little Vicky came rattling downstairs to kiss her gran good night.

But Doris couldn't avoid her daughter-in-law for ever. The moment came eventually, when they were both sitting in the living-room with a great silence — and only a few feet of space between them.

"Look, Mum . . ." Sally began suddenly.

"I don't think we have anything much to say to each other, Sally," said Doris, springing to her feet with the intention of switching on the television.

"But we have," Sally cried, putting out a detaining hand. "At least *I* have, Mum. I should have said it two years ago. But I couldn't bear to add to your hurt.

"It's only lately that I've come to my senses. That I've suddenly seen that I was depriving you of a grandchild, and Vicky of a grandmother."

"What are you talking about?" Doris asked, looking at the young woman coldly, but sitting down again on the edge of the settee.

"Mum, Tony didn't leave a lot of money. In fact, all he left behind him were debts. Masses of them," Sally said tightly. "He wasn't very . . . responsible. He took risks with the business that I knew nothing about. And he was extravagant."

172

The Truth Will Out . . .

"Stop it!" Doris clapped her hands to her ears. The room spun and she felt for a moment as though she couldn't breathe.

"Don't dare tell me those wicked lies!" She gasped, standing up and holding on to the back of the settee for support.

"Mum! Please! It's the *truth*. It doesn't mean that I loved Tony any the less.

"In fact, I probably loved him more," Sally began, her eyes bright with unshed tears.

But Doris wouldn't hear any more. She found her way blindly to the door and went stumblingly upstairs to her bedroom.

NEXT morning, Vicky, who alone had enjoyed a good night's sleep, was up bright and early. Sally, who had lain unhappily awake until dawn, was sound asleep when the little girl tiptoed out of the spare bedroom.

It took Vicky fifteen minutes to find her way into the living-room cupboard with its intriguing pile of multi-coloured bags and her grandmother's weaving frame. By the time Sally found her, she was hung about with bags like a Christmas tree.

And Doris's frame was lying in three pieces on the carpet.

"Oh, Vicky! You naughty girl! What have you done?" Sally cried in dismay as she ran over and picked up what was left of the frame. "Oh, your gran will be so upset. She really treasured this. Your daddy made it for her when he was a little boy."

"I didn't mean to!" Vicky wailed, a tear rolling down her pink cheek.

"Don't, darling! Don't cry!" Doris's voice rang out from the doorway.

She was white faced and shadowy eyed, and still in her dressing-gown. She hurried across the room and put her arms round Vicky.

"Granny doesn't mind, dear. Honestly!" she said.

She looked up at Sally, a faint pink stealing into her cheeks.

"Tony didn't make it," she said quietly. "He pretended that he had. But quite by accident I discovered from the mother of another boy that Tony had bought it from him. I never told Tony's father. I even pretended to myself . . ." Her voice cracked and faded.

Sally led the older woman across to the settee and sat down beside her.

"But it doesn't make any difference to how we felt about him, Mum? Does it?" she said gently.

"No," Doris whispered, gripping the young woman's hand tightly. "Of course it doesn't. Can you ever forgive me for the way I've behaved?"

But Sally's loving arms told Doris she was already forgiven. □

Printed and published in Great Britain by D. C. Thomson & Co., Ltd., Dundee, Glasgow and London. © D. C. Thomson & Co., Ltd., 1989.
While every reasonable care will be taken, neither D. C. Thomson & Co., Ltd., nor its agents will accept liability for loss or damage to colour transparencies or any other material submitted to this publication.

ISBN 085116-457-9